MAN AND
MASTIFF

Man and Mastiff

THE STORY OF THE ST. BERNARD DOG
THROUGH HISTORY

by Helen Kay

13713

THE MACMILLAN COMPANY, NEW YORK

COLLIER-MACMILLAN LIMITED, LONDON

ACKNOWLEDGMENTS

For help with translations from German, French, and Italian sources, I wish to thank my friends Gisela Quitzau, Eva Harrington, and Maria Bien.

For information on various aspects of archaeology, zoology, and history, thanks are due Dr. F. C. Fraser and Judith King of the British Museum of Natural History; Dr. Magnus Degerbøl of the University of Copenhagen; Dr. J. P. Scott, Research Professor at Bowling Green State University, Ohio. Other courtesies were extended by Professor D. H. Shahm, director of the Berne University Library; Jost Schmid of the Swiss Cynological Society at Berne, Switzerland; E. Kuyt of the Canadian Wildlife Service, Fort Smith, Northwest Territory, Canada; Millicent Selsam of New York City; Ernst Klarer of Weinfelden, Switzerland; Mr. and Mrs. Hans Böhi of Burgelen, Switzerland; and the brothers of the Hospice of the Great St. Bernard Pass.

Thanks, too, to the manager of the Beau Rivage at Geneva, who supplied us with the biggest bouquets of blue, pink, and white cornflowers, on arrival and departure; and to Paul Vuyet for the edelweiss, the white and woolly Alpine flowers, given us on leaving the Pass.

CONTENTS

I *

"The Highest in Animal Nature"

TIME: *the eighteenth century*
PLACE: *the top of Europe, at the Great St. Bernard Pass in the Alps of Switzerland*
CHARACTERS: *a lost traveler   a monk   a dog*

"The night falls. The snow falls. Alone, trembling . . . the traveler takes a few steps and is lost. . . . All is dark. He stops at the edge of a precipice. He does not dare to move forward or backward. Soon the cold penetrates. His bones stiffen. A deep sleep comes over him. His last thoughts are for his children and his wife . . .

"But is there not the ring of a bell? Or is this the sign of coming death which makes his senses hear imaginary sounds?

"No, it is true. He does hear something. Of what use, though? His feet cannot carry him further.

"Another noise . . . a dog is sniffing close. It comes closer. . . . It is there. It howls with joy. A hermit follows close behind."

"The Highest in Animal Nature"

These words were written by the French writer François René de Chateaubriand (1768-1848) when news about the rescue work of the monks and their dogs at the Great St. Bernard Pass was already well known to the world. Their fame had circled the globe and was one of the great wonders of the time, long before the days of telephone and telegraph.

The pass crosses the mountains between Italy and Switzerland at eighty-one hundred feet above sea level. A ring of peaks rises even higher, to 9,350 feet, forming a valley.

Here, even in the summertime, snow falls almost weekly, averaging thirty-six feet a year. In a saucer-like lake, frozen 265 days out of 365, only minnows live; these have been brought in recent years from the Little St. Bernard below. During the hottest days of summer, the temperature rises to only 60°F, and in the winter it falls to 22°F below zero. For nearly ten months of the year the Pass is snowbound.

In the eighteenth century—as today—an ancient hospice was a travelers' resting place maintained by an order of monks. There the monks' partners, a group of dogs raised and trained by them, followed and led, pulled and hauled, warned and warmed, guided and directed the helpless to the shelter.

The renowned rescue program of which Chateaubriand wrote was in fact a very small one. Only fifteen to twenty dogs were ever kept at the hospice at one time, and this number only in summer. About seven remained there dur-

Mountain snowstorm pictured in the nineteenth century

ing the long winter. Each year a few new dogs were trained to continue the work.

What the monks and their dogs did as a service to man for hundreds of years provided an inspiration that others were to follow. The pioneer program at the Pass—of breeding and training dogs for rescue service—became the model for training other dogs to function in humanitarian ways.

The Newfoundland dog, both a strong swimmer and a great retriever, was used to rescue men at sea. The German Shepherd became a seeing-eye to the human blind. The

A St. Bernard, popularly known as Switzerland's National Dog

bloodhound, because of its distinctive and strong sense of smell, led the way to persons lost in isolated woods and parks. In two World Wars, dogs became dogs of mercy, Red Cross dogs, medics trained to rescue men from the field of battle. These dogs dragged the wounded from danger spots where a man could not, or dared not, go.

The most massive of all the working breeds is the St. Bernard. On its hind legs it stands as tall as a six-foot man. It weighs at least 160 pounds when full grown, and frequently reaches 200 pounds. From the ground to the shoulders it stands at least twenty-eight inches high, more often thirty or thirty-one inches. It has white, red, and streaked markings, known as brindle. Its facial expression is benevolent, its character gentle.

Until the mid-nineteenth century, the large dogs of the St. Bernard Pass had no real name. They were called *Talhund*, valley dog, *Alpenhund*, dog of the Alps, "butcher dog," Alpine mastiff, saint dog, convent dog, or "dog of the Lord." Mostly, though, they were known as *Barihund*, or Barry dogs. This was no nickname for Bernard but was inspired, rather, by the dog's bearlike appearance. The German word for bear is *baer*, and local dialect made it *Bari*, little bear. The German word for dog is *hund*, our hound. For many years, the dogs of the hospice were known simply as *Barihund*.

They *earned* their name, St. Bernard, through their work.

When General Lafayette sent a pair to a United States postmaster in the early days of the new republic, he wrote: "a symbol of the highest in animal nature."

2 ✳

Experiment at the
Top of the World

JUST HOW did the monks and the dogs get to the top of Europe?

The large dogs came first, two thousand years ago, when the Romans crossed the Alps by way of the Pennine Pass ("pennine" is an ancient Celtic word for summit). They came with the invaders to conquer the people beyond the mountain. They came as battle dogs, sentry dogs, fierce fighters accompanying men of war.

The monks came a thousand years later to bring peace to the mountains. Pilgrims passing over the summit, ordinary travelers, merchants, workers in pursuit of their livelihood were being harassed by brigands. The monks came to help human beings in trouble.

The Pennine Pass was the path used by conquerors and invaders, north and south. From here Hannibal crossed into Italy in 218 B.C., with elephants. Some say the Pennine Alps were named for this Carthaginian soldier, since "Poenus" in Latin means Carthaginian. When the Helvetii (the people who lived in what we know as Switzerland) sought new lands beyond the Jura in 58 B.C., Caesar went to conquer them, then turned to the rest of Gaul. Forty years later the Roman Army occupied the whole of the valley up to the Rhine. By 12 B.C. Augustus made a road, at some points as wide as 12¼ feet, across the Alps to join Aosta and Martigny. The Greek geographer Strabo had written: "Here no wheeled traffic could go."

At the top, the Romans built a temple to the chief of all their gods—Jupiter—the god of thunder. Nearby, they built a refuge for their legionaries, whose mission it was to guard the Pass. And they may have built kennels here, as well— for when they conquered all of Gaul, they brought with them massive war dogs, among others.

These dogs, called Molossers by the Romans, were strong and lionlike—and in fact they had been lion-fighters as well as warriors in the land from which they came.

The word "Molosser" had a Greek origin. The Molossians were the mother tribe and Molossia was the home in northern Greece of the great Greek soldier, Alexander, who conquered the world in 327 B.C. His mother, Olympias, was the daughter of the King of Epirus, of which Molossia was an important part. Alexander found the great dogs first in Asia Minor. Sent back to the mainland, the dogs were given his motherland's name, Molossians. From Greece the dogs went on to Rome. Later, Roman soldiers took them everywhere, since they had already been trained as war

dogs in those far countries that Alexander had conquered.

By 100 A.D. the Roman Molosser was used to guard all the mountain passes and military stations in Switzerland, Austria, and the Balkans. Aelian, who, around 200 A.D., wrote on the nature of animals, said: "The soldiers wept over their dogs slain in war." By then the animals had earned a new Roman name: *mansuetinus*, meaning tame, which eventually became "mastiff."

In the third century, when the Romans began retreating from the mountainous lands they had forcibly occupied, they left their dogs behind. Some of these had mated with local breeds and left their puppies. Others were let loose in the rout of defeat. So the war dogs remained, wherever they could find someone to feed them. They made the surrounding valleys below the Pass of Mont-Joux, the French equivalent of the Roman original, literally "Jupiter's Pass," their home.

Opposite:
Hannibal's troops at Pennine Pass

Right:
Statue of a Molosser

Hundreds of years went by, however, before the mastiffs became rescue dogs.

Just how did the transformation happen? How did the St. Bernard, renowned for dignity and intelligence, gentleness and benevolence, evolve from these fierce dogs of war?

Professor Albert Heim of Switzerland, in a talk to the St. Bernard judges in April, 1927, said: "Years of inbreeding with particular emphasis being placed on achieving qualifications necessary for the rescue work in the mountains have produced the St. Bernard of today."

That was the physical dog. But for the origin of its service in the mountains we must turn to a group of men, the masters and trainers of the dog, who founded the highest populated settlement in Europe.

Father Bernard was preaching at the Cathedral of Aosta on the Italian side of the Pass of Mont-Joux in the early eleventh century. Here, foot-weary pilgrims came to him weeping, their clothing torn and tattered, their heads bruised and bloody. They told Father Bernard that they had been attacked in the mountains by brigands. They had been robbed, and some of their number had been murdered.

Brigands and pirates had been harassing travelers in the mountains for a long time. Murder, robbery, and ransom had become a kind of toll of the Pass. Bernard decided that the toll must end. He would fight it. He went to live in the heights and dedicated himself to the welfare of all travelers.

For many hundreds of years the great Pass was one of the few routes across the mountains. Merchants—their goods strapped to their backs—used it, heading north or south to sell their wares. Journeymen used it, too, on their way to find work with their special trades and skills.

In later years, the travelers were mostly Italian agricultural workers going to pick crops in France and Switzerland. When the work in the fields and vineyards was finished, there was a great rush from the north to get back to Italy. They made a steady stream, the tide changing only with the seasons, north in the early summer, south in the late summer—before the snowfall: twenty-five thousand men, women, and children each year. Frequently they carried all their worldly goods with them. They were poor people in a hurry. They did not have places to stay in the countries to the north once the harvest was gathered. In order to exist, they had to cross the Pass as soon as the thaws came and return home before the winter set in.

In Father Bernard's time, whatever the reason to travel, this was still the only way: on foot and over the summit.

In 1049 Bernard built a hospice, as a home and haven for mountain travelers. Here all the hungry, the hurt, the weary, and the cold were cared for. Here anyone could rest on his journey—eat, drink, and get a good night's sleep. To continue the work he founded an order of brothers. For this, Bernard became sainted. Ultimately, the Pass was given his name, St. Bernard, and the shelter, the Hospice of St. Bernard.

The Baron of Menthon, his father, gave of his great wealth

The Hospice of St. Bernard (after a painting by Turner)

so that food and shelter were provided free to all who came to the Hospice. With these funds the buildings were expanded. Some parts stand to this day.

The Pass became free again. Soon it was open to all—

even to the brigands, who as such seemed to disappear from the mountains.

Even after the danger of bandits was over, the monks stayed on in their Hospice. For their true work had only begun. There were still other, greater dangers to be met. These were not man-made; these were nature's dangers, constant and terrifying—"the white death."

The monks became guides over the summit of Europe. They led travelers down from the Hospice and up the narrow path in all weather. When there were accidents—due to slides, snowstorms, sleet—they rescued the victims.

No one knows just when the dogs became joint workers with the monks, since all records were burned in a fire at the Hospice in 1555. A painting of St. Bernard with a dog, very like the St. Bernard of today, does exist, but some think it was painted much later, after the legend was well established.

The early monks may well have been given a dog to keep them company in their lonely vigil here. Perhaps the first was a watchdog from the estates of the Baron of Menthon in Savoy, at the foot of the mountains. It is known that only the landed gentry could keep dogs as big as the descendants of the Roman mastiffs. No villager or farmer could have afforded the more than two pounds of food a day that such a dog requires.

From a later time—1350—there exists a coat of arms of a family called De Hailigberg. On it is a face of a dog like the great St. Bernard. If such a family did exist, they might

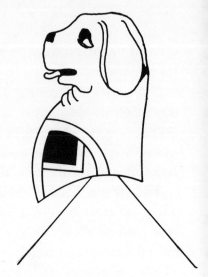

Ink sketch of the
De Hailigberg coat of arms

well have been keepers of the massive animals. But since no other record can be found, it has been suggested that perhaps the insigne is rather that of the family of brothers itself, since De Hailigberg means "the Holy Mountain" in German.

The dog of the Alps was described as both good-natured and clumsy by St. Jerome in 1414 in a word picture: "the good tempered old Alpine mastiff whose clumsy dew-clawed heels were liable to do more mischief than they had any idea of doing with their teeth."

An oil painting of a dog alone, catching a scent in the wind, hangs in the Hospice hall to this day. This picture of a rescue dog, dated 1695, was painted by an Italian artist of the time, Salvator Rosa. The dog already looks like our St. Bernard.

However the relationship occurred, it seems agreed that

14

companionship came first. Teamwork between man and dog came later.

The monks, hard-working themselves, soon began to give their *baris* simple tasks. The dogs performed these chores well. Then the brothers began taking them along on their errands of mercy in the mountains. They noticed that the dogs were reliable workers, and easily trained. Moreover, the monks saw that the dogs seemed to know where the path lay under new-fallen snow. They could lead the way back to the Hospice in fog, sleet, snow, and rain, when man was uncertain which way to go in the all-white world. They could find and follow the scent of a man on the trail.

The animals were by that time being used commonly as work-dogs in the valley below. On the large estates they became watchdogs, still called *Alpenhund*; in the villages they were called "butcher dogs." The name originated because of the great quantity of meat the dogs needed: only

Salvator Rosa's painting of an ancestor of the St. Bernard

a butcher could afford to keep them. Usually, the dogs were expected to pull their little carts through the streets and alleys of the medieval villages, delivering the meat.

At the Hospice, Canon Vincent Camos had four hundred visitors to cook for and feed in a single day of 1708. He solved his work problem by having a "wheel constructed where a dog was put in to turn the skewer."

The large dogs were used to carry provisions to the Hospice from the village of Banches, a distance of eighteen miles. Hospice records of 1815 report that 112 pounds of provisions were saddled to the mastiff's back.

*An early friar of
the Hospice with his dog*

Some of the dogs would follow the monks' servants to the stables, carrying empty bottles strapped to either side. The servants would then fill them with milk and butter; the dogs would return the food to the Hospice kitchen.

By doing simple chores, the dogs learned to be man's helpers. But it was the rescue program that began man and dog's true partnership. The holy brothers were devoted to the travelers and concerned with their safety. The dogs were devoted to their masters, the brothers. The close relationship of the two made possible the humanitarian work done at the Great St. Bernard Pass.

Recorded at the Hospice are the names of more than two thousand persons saved by the Barry dogs in their long years of service.

3 ✳

At the Pass—
Two Hundred Years Ago

TODAY, most of the monks at the Hospice of St. Bernard are excellent skiers.

In 1883 a visitor to the Pass left a gift of a single pair of skis. The sport was just becoming popular in Europe, having spread to all the snowy lands from its home in the far north. Six years later the monks owned a dozen pairs and they incorporated ski racing as a part of their training. They began to use skis on their rounds of work, because skis were swift and efficient for locating the lost or injured in the snow.

However, in the eighteenth century, the holy brothers did all their work on foot.

In 1708 Prior Ballalu described how travelers made the journey over the Pass in the winter, how they were met and guided up and down the mountain:

"Every year from November to May 15th, at 8 A.M., when the days are longer, and at 9 A.M. when they are short, the 'hospitalier' [the monk from the Hospice who would act as guide] went to a small cave which is on the Bourg-St. Pierre side . . . to help the mountain travelers.

"At the same time he guided down those who stayed in the house. . . . With him, when he leaves, he always takes some bread and the brother in charge of wine gives him a bottle. He offers all he meets a drink, but first to those

St. Bernard dogs with Père Econome, a monk at the Hospice

who have no strength left to get to the monastery, and to the poor.

"He carries a large stick, long as a pike, to help him when he walks through the snow. There is almost never a year during which one or more do not die of illness or are taken by surprise by avalanches or cold before they could be brought up here."

As early as 1707 the Hospice records noted that one of its dogs was lost while on a rescue mission. By the middle of the eighteenth century such losses were so great—of both men and dogs—that the naturalist Marc–Theodore Bourrit of Geneva wrote: "Most of the priests have been killed by avalanches. Also many of the large dogs who have been trained for assisting the travelers. . . ."

Only once in all the years at the Hospice did the dogs do guard duty—but in a reverse kind of way.

One day more than a century ago the Hospice was besieged by bandits. The thieves demanded that the Prior hand over his safe. Instead the Prior led the thieves to the kennels and showed them his dogs. The ruffians took one look at the mastiffs and fled.

In 1800 Canon Murith described the great dogs as follows: "Our mastiffs, who are so useful to the traveler, are of an extraordinary size. . . . They bark from far and cuddle when they come near. They even recognize at a certain depth the traces of the old road from which it would be dangerous to get away, when fresh snow has fallen on top. . . .

"Our dogs are never afraid of the cold. Nature covers them for the climate in which they live."

"Those dogs that were so famous all over Europe" impressed Pastor Bridel so vividly that he wrote of his unforgettable visit to the Hospice in 1801 when he returned to his home in the valley. "One cannot get close enough to this lovely and precious breed. Their color is reddish, mixed with white. Their disposition is sweet. They never bite and bark rarely when travelers arrive. They go often, alone, to meet them at the foot of the mountain. They hug them; guide them and lead them to the monastery.

"It is wrong, however, to believe that they owe their talent to nature only, or that they train each other. The Fathers train for this work and this training requires a great amount of care and patience. It is true that the small ones easily copy what they learn from the older dogs. This breed loves . . . to roll in the freshly fallen snow. . . ."

Man and mastiff in an Alpine blizzard

4 ✻

Why There Is
Always a Barry

FOR YEARS, all the dogs at the Pass were Barry dogs, but there was only one Barry.

Anna Maria Vincenti learned this, though she told no one in words.

The winter of 1806 came in with a blizzard. The snow fell early, was heavy, and stayed late. It was recorded as one of the most terrible of winters—in a world where winter is always a terror.

Anna Maria Vincenti was a young widow, and she waited at the foot of the mountain for the fresh spring and an end to the snow. In the preceding year she had come to Switzerland with her husband. Together they had labored in the fields all summer. As they were ready to return to Italy and home, her husband fell ill and died. The snows came. It was too late to cross the mountains. Food and lodging for herself and her small child over the winter consumed whatever money she had saved. Finally, March 20 arrived, and it seemed to be spring below the mountain. Anna Maria decided to begin the long walk home with her little son, before they both died of hunger. She had nothing left.

She knew there were shelters to rest in along the way from Bourg-St. Pierre to the top of the mountain. There she could stay at the Hospice. The monks would feed her. Later, she could descend to the Italian side and home.

With the child in her arms she began the ascent. She did not know that up there it had snowed in the night. Up there it was still winter.

At the Hospice, Barry and Brother Luigi, his master, went on their regular rounds. Twice a day, every morning and every evening, the monks, their servants, and their dogs made a normal round of the paths to see if there were travelers in distress coming to or from Italy and Switzerland.

Brother Luigi was Barry's trainer. He walked with a long stick. Barry, six years old, and an experienced mountain rescuer, went where he wished—but never too far from his master. Of all the dogs he had ever trained, Brother Luigi loved Barry best. There had never been a smarter dog at the Pass.

Barry was the largest. Big as a bear, he had developed a particularly strong hugging technique. To someone in the snow, overcome with lassitude, wanting only to sleep forever in its numbing whiteness, this hug could mean life.

The warmth of the dog's body would revive the fallen traveler. Barry's wet tongue, licking the sleeping one, might stir him. Then Barry could help the victim save himself.

The first Barry as he appears today at a Berne museum

On this cold, bright morning of March, after the evening snow, Barry seemed uneasy. Since Brother Luigi had trained him from puppyhood, he knew how Barry behaved under all conditions. They went on their regular pattern of search —Brother Luigi with his big stick probing the freshly fallen snow, and Barry sniffing . . . sniffing . . . as though he had caught a scent. Suddenly the great dog stopped. He was listening, head high. Not a muscle quivered.

Brother Luigi stopped, too, wondering: What does Barry hear? A mountain rabbit on such a bright morning? What scent was in the wind? Did someone need his help? Brother

Luigi could neither hear nor smell what the dog was already warned of. The monk waited patiently, since he respected Barry's senses. He knew that if the dog was disturbed, there must be a reason. Silently, he stood motionless in the snow beside Barry.

Suddenly a sound like thunder blasted the mountain stillness. Brother Luigi threw himself down next to the dog. When the roar stopped and with it the rush of snow, Brother Luigi raised his head, then stood up. They had been lucky. The avalanche had passed them by.

Now they must return to the Hospice and let the Prior know that they were safe. Brother Luigi started back, but Barry would not move. He would not follow his master. He seemed to be listening, still. Brother Luigi couldn't budge the dog. Exhausted, he finally gave up and went home alone. He felt sure Barry would follow later.

Barry did not return that night.

Back at the Hospice the Prior worried about the missing lead dog. Barry was such an experienced rescuer, the Prior felt, that the dog must want help, must be following the trail of someone who needed him. He sent other monks with other dogs to find Barry. They searched all day long and into the following night. It was dark and bitterly cold. The monks had looked up and down the familiar paths, but they could find no trace of Barry. They returned to the Hospice. The next day they would try again. Perhaps, perhaps he would return on his own four powerful legs. . . .

In the morning they set out again. Again they could find

nothing: neither Barry nor any victim of the avalanche.

Late that evening the Prior himself went in search of Barry. No sooner had he closed the door of the Hospice behind him, and recovered from the first sting of the cold night air, than he saw the missing dog huddling against the side of the building. The dog moved slowly, and in a strange way.

Was he hurt?

As the Prior came closer, he saw that the dog seemed heavily burdened. A bundle was tied to his back, and it was packed with snow, frozen stiff. The Prior pulled Barry and his bundle into the warm Hospice kitchen. He unwrapped a woman's shawl, which secured the bundle to Barry's back. Then the Prior understood why the dog had walked so oddly. The bundle was a small child.

The monks breathed into the child's mouth; they rubbed his body with snow. His lips began to move; he was crying now. The boy was alive.

This was the child of Anna Maria Vincenti, the young Italian widow who had tried to walk home over the mountains. Her child was saved . . . but she had been lost in the avalanche. Somehow, when Barry found her she still had the strength to tie her child to the big dog's back.

The rescue of the boy made Barry's name a legend.

But he was already the lead dog, and behind him was a long list of rescued. Barry was only the best of a line of champions.

Barry was born in 1800, the year Napoleon crossed the

Napoleon's soldiers crossing the Great St. Bernard Pass in 1800

Alps with forty thousand men on his way to Italy to cut off the Austrians. Barry's father was among the rescue dogs there at the time.

It was May, when Napoleon's soldiers were dragging their heavy cannon up the mountain and over the snow.

Suddenly, near the summit, ten men slipped soundlessly down the slope to what seemed certain doom. Both cannoneers and cannon were caught in a crevasse. It seemed as though no one could reach them. Officers rushed to the

Hospice for help; dogs and monks were sent to the rescue.

The men were saved. They were hauled up and set on the path, then brought back to the Hospice and nursed.

It is said that Napoleon himself rubbed the dogs' backs and patted their heads in gratitude. Engravings commemorate this great military crossing.

In appreciation of both man and mastiff, Napoleon arranged to finance a similar hospice at the Simplon Pass. It exists to this day.

Brother Luigi had been trainer to all these dogs. With Barry he had worked for nine years. The two were inseparable.

One day, while on a routine mission, Brother Luigi became lost. The monks opened the kennel door. "Find Brother Luigi," they told Barry. "Find your master."

The dog followed his master's scent. He found Brother Luigi in a gorge, covered over with snow. Barry slid down beside him, but he could not pull Brother Luigi out. No one knows if Brother Luigi was still alive, but Barry acted as he had been trained to act; he ran for help. The dog returned to the Hospice. His head was low; his tail hung between his legs. He howled. He pulled at the Prior's cloak. He spoke with all the language a dog can manage, and the monks followed.

But it was too late for Brother Luigi.

Barry and the other dogs, led by other monks, continued on their daily morning and evening rounds. New masters came; they continued to train new dogs. The rescue work went on—day after day, month after month, year after year—in all seasons. There was hardly a year that passed without someone owing his life to this work.

By 1812, six years after that most terrible winter, and three years after Brother Luigi died, Barry was twelve years old. He, alone, had rescued forty persons. This was to be his last working year. He was now a very old dog—having performed ten years of service in a climate and at an altitude that shortened most other dogs' life spans from fourteen to ten years.

Once again, Napoleon was raising an army. The mountains were full of young men evading his call to arms. Those who did not wish to fight were taking refuge in the hills in order to escape their military service.

One farmer's son, named Martin, went to the summit with a loaf of bread and a large knife. The bread was eaten soon enough. But the knife might still come in handy.

As he wandered over the paths of ice and snow, an avalanche trapped him. Martin could not move. He could only scream for help.

Barry heard him. The monks and the dogs were on their regular rounds, and he was the first to reach the frightened young man.

As he had been trained to do, he dug around the boy with his paws, partly freeing him. Then, trying to keep him warm until help arrived, he nestled close, put his big bearlike face against the boy's face. Maddened with fear, the boy imagined that Barry was indeed a bear trying to eat him. He drew his knife from his jacket and lashed out. He hit at the dog again and again, cutting through his thick short fur and into the skin.

Fortunately the monks and the other dogs were not far behind Barry. When they found him, the rescuers saw that both boy and dog needed help.

"A bear is eating me!" Martin screamed, fighting the dog who had pulled him from the snow.

The monks wept for Barry. For the snow was stained with his blood. Two stayed to help the boy, to dress Barry's wounds. A third sped to the Hospice for stretchers and more hands to haul both victims home: the boy, victim of the snow, and the dog, victim of the boy.

Barry did live. He was glorified in story and painting. He wore medals on his collar, and ribbons hung in his honor in the Hospice hall. However, the monks decided that Barry had earned a rest. Life at the Hospice was too rugged for their convalescing hero. He was retired to the city of Berne, where he lived another two years. He died there in 1814, and his body was stuffed and placed in the Berne Museum of Natural History. It stands there to this day, proudly greeting all.

Almost a hundred years later, another dog was named Barry II. Strong and tall, he was leader of the team of rescue dogs. He wore around his neck a chain which dragged when he went on his rounds. Travelers in distress could grab the chain, and he would guide them to the Hospice. He was strong enough to pull a man; steady enough to hold him up if he stumbled.

But Barry II disappeared one day into a snow-covered chasm. The monks marked the date in their records: May 20, 1905. He had died in the prime of his life.

Five years later, Barry III became the lead dog at the Hospice. Neither as tall nor as strong as those who bore the name earlier, he was nonetheless a sure-footed guide to those who traveled the mountain paths. Such is the deceptiveness of the seemingly soft white world, however, that he, too, became its victim. The monks found Barry III wedged into a narrow gorge, frozen. His stuffed body stands today in the great hall of the Hospice.

From 1910 on, the monks have always had a Barry. The most beautiful male dog, the pick of the litter, the son of the sire, the prize dog, the quickest to learn, the most intelligent—the one who might be leader of the pack—this dog earns the name Barry.

There is one there today spelled Bari, for bear.

Only as recently as the dog exhibition at Birmingham, England, in 1862, were the *Barihund*, the Barry dogs, officially given a name and designated a breed. From that day on, they became known everywhere as the great St. Bernards.

So it came to be that the saint who named the Pass also named the dogs.

5 *

What Is a Dog?

"St. Bernard," then, is a very recent name. Following the trail of the big dog in search of its beginnings, we must travel back in time, passing into archaeology where written history leaves off.

One theory holds that the origins of the large mastiff that we know can be traced to faraway Tibet, where, in fact, a great, dark, bold mastiff exists today. Some think this dog is the ancestor of the Molosser, and hence the St. Bernard.

Marco Polo, merchant of Venice, journeyed beyond Tibet in the thirteenth century on his way to the lands of silk and spices. He wrote of the great dogs he saw. "These people of Tibet have mastiff dogs as big as donkeys, capital in seizing wild beasts." He described the breed as so "fierce and bold that two of them together will attack a lion."

While in the realm of Kublai Khan, Marco Polo also reported on "the glorious sight" when the Prince went hunting, and how the great dogs worked, with "2,000 men each in charge of one or more mastiffs."

The Tibetan Mastiff, though dark, looks very like the St. Bernard, with its large skull, powerful body, pendant ears, thick, short coat of hair, and short muzzle. Perhaps because the two mountainous areas, the Himalayas and the Alps, are so alike, similar dogs could thrive in both. The great nineteenth-century scientist Charles Darwin, in his book *The Variation of Animals and Plants Under Domestication*, reported, however, that the "Tibet Mastiff degenerated when it migrated on the plains of India and can only live in the mountains."

Dogs attacking a deer (sculpture c. A.D. 79 from Herculaneum)

Clay tablet of a mastiff with an Assyrian soldier

Dogs of huge bulk and bone with heavy heads and pendulous ears were kept twenty-five hundred years ago by the King of Assyria on the plains of Asia Minor. At the British Museum, which has on exhibit the palace of the great ruler Ashurbanipal (669-626 B.C.) from Calak, Assyria, mastiffs of this type are shown. Harnessed for war, their fierceness was fabled.

"When a dog entereth a palace and lieth upon a bed, that palace, no man shall capture," was a saying.

Besides the sport of war, the Assyrian rulers enjoyed lion

hunting. The mastiffs were expert performers and could fearlessly track down and battle the king of the beasts.

Five different clay tablets show the mastiffs at work in ancient Assyria. On some of the tablets are scenes showing the dog's ability to: "cause evil to come forth," "nose out a thief," "bite his enemies," and "protect his master."

Herodotus, the Father of History, who lived from 484 to 425 B.C., wrote that the income of four cities was used to support these dogs. Each dog needed two sila of bread a day (about two quarts), and the villages worked to supply this daily ration.

One of the tablets shows a dog on leash: sturdy, with a large head and long ears, he is ready for combat. The soldier at his side is armed but holds the dog tightly while the dog strains to attack. Beside the mastiff the soldier looks like a small boy.

A medieval war dog

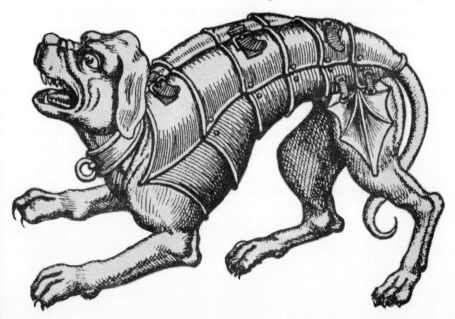

A hundred years after Herodotus, Alexander the Great invaded Asia Minor, and the dogs were still there to be admired. To keep fit between battles Alexander went on great hunting expeditions, accompanied by beloved dogs, raised and trained for lion hunting. When a favorite died in India, he named a town after it—Peritas.

Alexander died abroad, but the dogs sent home thrived as hunters, sheepherders, and dogs of war in Molossia. The first 156 Molossian dogs went from here to the arenas of Rome to be exhibited and to fight the lions. Later, the Romans took the huge dogs through the Pennine Pass in the Alps, where our story of the St. Bernard began.

By 39 B.C. a Greek coin honored the Molosser with an imprint.

Professor Conrad Gesner in his *Animal History* of 1551, published in Zurich, described the Molossian dogs: "They are said to be very big and fierce, and to be used equally as hunting dogs, as sheep dogs and in warfare." In Gesner's day the dogs were already called "mastinus," from the Latin *mansuetinus,* and almost mastiff. It was obvious that the great war dogs could be trained—either as hunters or as sheep dogs.

The second theory sends the great dogs to Tibet from Asia Minor.

Dr. J. P. Scott, who has written much on the relationship of dog and man, says: "There is no reason for believing that breeds which are similar to each other and are found in different parts of the world are necessarily related. For example, the Tibetan Mastiff might be quite unrelated to other large dogs. If they are related, it is perhaps more likely that the large war dogs were first developed in Mesopotamia and spread to other areas."

But to understand the dog we must search deeper into the past, asking the question, "Just what is a dog?"

To find the answer we must go back to the order Carnivora, meat eater; to the dog family itself, Canidae; and to the particular genus, Canis. The scientific name of the domesticated dog is *Canis familiaris*. His distant ancestor—the wild ancestor of all dogs—is the wolf, *Canis lupus*.

6 *

Mother Wolf

CHARLES DARWIN thought dogs were of such size and variety that they must surely have evolved from several different animals. "Looking at the domestic dogs of the whole world, I have after laborious collection of facts come to the conclusion that several wild species of Canidae have been tamed and that their blood, in some cases mingled, flows in the veins of our domestic breeds."

There have been many generations of dogs, however, and their breeding has been controlled by men to develop specific traits of size, conformation, and temperament: dogs as small as the Chihuahua, weighing only a few pounds— toy dogs, pets; dogs born short-legged like the Dachshund, deformed in some way and bred for its peculiarities; dogs born with a foreshortened nose, like the English Bulldog, and bred for the sport of bull-baiting once popular in England; dogs as strong as the St. Bernard, massive, gentle— mastiffs in the Roman sense, tamed.

It is easy to see how Darwin came to his conclusion, but

All domesticated breeds of dog—from the Bulldog (Top Left) *to the St. Bernard* (Bottom Right)—*are now thought to be descended from the wolf.*

most scientists today name the wolf as the ancestor of all dogs.

The *Canis lupus* ranges over all of Europe and Asia and throughout North America from Greenland to Mexico. In South America, Africa, and Australia there are other types. The largest and the strongest of all is the North American wolf. Through the lupi differ, in texture of fur, color, and size, they are very much alike. Mostly their color is gray. There are brown and black wolves, with variations, and in the Arctic North, there is the white wolf.

The classic picture of the wolf at bay is the hungry wolf. Jack London opens his novel *White Fang* by showing the despair of men trying to outrun a starving wolf pack:

North American timber wolves in Minnesota lake country

An Arctic wolf

". . . Henry, who was now traveling behind the sled, emitted a low warning whistle. Bill turned and looked, then quietly stopped the dogs. To the rear, from around the last bend and plainly into view, on the very trail they had just covered, trotted a furry slinking form. Its nose was to the trail, and it trotted with a peculiar sliding, effortless gait. When they halted, it halted, throwing up its head and regarding them steadily with nostrils that twitched as it caught and studied the scent of them.

" 'It's the she-wolf,' Bill whispered."

His cold fear was a foretaste of death. In the story all the Eskimo dogs and one of the men are eaten.

Scientists, however, though respectful of the wolf's predatory character, have studied the wolf and have found it tamable.

Juliet Clutton-Brock, in her paper on the origins of the dog, has written: "The northern wolf is not the fierce untamable beast that legend has reputed him to be."

Lois Crisler, in her *Arctic Wild*, has shown how dog-like the large wolves of the Canadian North can become. She and her husband raised them.

The scientist Adolph Murie, who traveled seventeen hundred miles on foot, and more on skis, studied and wrote on the home life of a wolf family at Mt. McKinley:

"Just as a laboring husband comes home to the family each evening after working all day, so do the wolves come home each morning after working all night. The wolf comes home tired, too, for he has traveled far in his hunting. Ten or fifteen miles is a usual jaunt for a hunt and he generally takes part in some chases in which he exerts himself tremendously . . . up and down slopes and ridges. When he arrives at the den he flops, relaxes completely and may not change his position for three or four hours."

The mother wolf meanwhile guarded the den and her nursing cubs. The other adults of the wolf pack brought food from miles away. On three occasions when the mother joined the hunt, another female remained behind in the den with the pups.

Another scientist, Farley Mowat of the Canadian Wildlife Service, wrote a book on the same subject, *Never Cry Wolf*. He tells of his own experiences observing a wolf family in its lair.

Three timber wolf pups

From his tent hideout, Mowat watched the parents busy with their young cubs. Here, too, they left another wolf in charge when the mother joined the hunt. They brought back food already half-digested—enough to feed four or five cubs—and regurgitated it for them.

At first they fed the cubs on mice and other small animals which abounded. But with the return of the caribou, in late summer, the hunting season began. By this time even the cubs could be trained to join in the hunt; the pack was a family group. In an organized way they attacked the weakest of the caribou, killing what they needed for food.

There were many occasions when Mowat thought he was observing the wolves, but in fact they were observing him from his most vulnerable position—from behind him. Yet they never attacked.

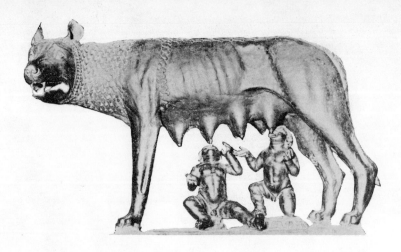

Romulus and Remus suckling the mother wolf, Lupa

Animals which have not learned to become frightened of man are not instinctively afraid of him, or even hostile. Charles Darwin wrote: "It deserves notice, as bearing on other animals as well as on the dog, that at an extremely ancient period, when man first entered any country, the animals living there would have felt no instinctive . . . fear of him, and would consequently have been tamed more easily than at present. . . . For instance, when the Falkland Islands were first visited by man, the large wolf-like dog *Canis antarcticus* fearlessly came to meet Byron's sailors."

Farley Mowat found an Eskimo, a native naturalist in the Canadian North, who claims to have spent a full twenty-four hours in a wolf den. His father put him there as a small child. He lived to tell the tale, and as an adult he even learned the meaning of the different wolf howls.

Perhaps the story of Romulus and Remus, the co-founders of Rome, is an ancient glorification of the gentleness of a mother wolf.

According to the legend, Mars, the god of war, loved Silvia, a vestal daughter. She bore him two fine twin boys. One day they were stolen and thrown into the marsh. Here, amid the bulrushes, Lupa, a female wolf, warmed and nursed the boys until a shepherd's wife found them. The twins grew up to be leaders of the shepherds. They built a city on the marshes where they had been nourished by the wolf. To this day, a statue of the twin boys standing beneath and suckling the wolf is the symbol of the great city of Rome.

A dog will also allow her puppies to suckle in this way —standing up.

Most naturalists are convinced that if you start with a wolf puppy, you will raise an animal that acts like a domesticated dog.

In fact, Adolph Murie entered the wolf den once, when the mother had gone to get food. Inside he found the six puppies. He picked up three and brought them out to the light. They were about a week old, and their eyes were still closed. All three were females. Murie returned two and adopted the smallest, the runt, and took her back with him to camp.

This puppy cried for a few days, but she soon became happy on bottled milk. When the nipple proved inconvenient for the large wolf mouth, she learned to lap milk out of a saucer. The puppy was placed on a chain in the yard and was very friendly and playful. She earned the name of Wags and became "the most friendly dog I have ever known," said Murie.

The adult wolves came several times to lure her back to the den and the wild. She would have gone, too, but she was chained. The wolf grew rapidly, and at a year and a half measured 27½ inches at the shoulder.

Another biologist with the Canadian Wildlife Service, E. Kuyt, has raised several wolf cubs. He says: "Wolf cubs can be raised like dogs if they are taken at an early age. I have seen female wolves with their cubs on several occasions. Once, I watched a female suckle her five young just outside the den. Another time, I saw a female carry a cub across a river, while a second pup swam behind mother on his own power. I have dug out nine occupied wolf dens, tagging thirty-one cubs in total. In all cases, both parents were present, and frequently other wolves as well. Sometimes, the female was surprised in the den when we started excavations.

"On two memorable occasions she [the mother] escaped by running between my legs. Never did a wolf even attempt or bluff an attack. I am concerned about running into grizzlies with cubs, but not wolves."

Kuyt is convinced that proper handling of a wolf will raise a fine social creature. He trusts them more than he trusts the Eskimo dog—perhaps, he admitted, "mostly because Eskimo dogs are mistreated and improperly trained."

Buck, the fictional dog hero of Jack London's *Call of the Wild*, made to work as a sled dog, was driven back to the wilderness by man's brutality, by the law of "club and fang."

Buck's father, Elmo, was a gentle St. Bernard; his mother, Shep, was a Scotch Shepherd dog.

"But for the stray brown on his muzzle and above his eyes and for the splash of white hair that ran midmost down his chest, he might well have been mistaken for a gigantic wolf, larger than the largest of the breed. From his St. Bernard father he had inherited size and weight, but it was his shepherd mother who had given shape to that size and weight. His muzzle was the long wolf muzzle, save that it was larger than the muzzle of any wolf; and his head, somewhat broader, was the wolf head on a massive scale.

"His cunning was wolf cunning and wild cunning; his intelligence shepherd intelligence and St. Bernard intelligence; and all this, plus an experience gained in the fiercest of schools, made him as formidable a creature as any that roamed the wild. . . .

"John Thornton was dead. The last tie was broken. Man and the claims of man no longer bound him. . . ."

In the wild, dogs and wolves interbreed freely. Eskimo dogs are almost always part wild wolf. Pliny, the Roman historian, said that the Gauls tied their female dogs in the woods that they might cross with wolves.

Both wolves and dogs have a pregnancy cycle of about sixty-three days. They are both born blind and remain so for nine days after birth. The wolf and the dog both have milk teeth, and their moulting period is the same. In fact, their structure, bone for bone, is so similar that it is difficult for zoologists to determine which is dog and which is wolf when their remains are found in prehistoric sites.

7 *

Was It a Dog or a Wolf?

Bone remains at early settlements can keep zoologists guessing.

At Star Carr in Yorkshire, England, in 1948, scientists unearthed some teeth and animal bones—part of a skull, a tibia (a shinbone), a femur (a thighbone)—that posed an interesting riddle. Answering this riddle involved some discoveries made in Denmark, on the Baltic Sea, and some investigations made by a Danish professor.

There was a time, long ago, when England was joined to Europe. The great Baltic Sea was merely a fresh-water lake. This was in the Mesolithic Age, the prehistoric Middle Stone Age, ten thousand years ago. During this period, the world was undergoing great climate changes. The last Ice Age was ending. Along the shores of that vast inland lake, settlements were forming.

We know this now because one day, a little over a hundred years ago, a Danish landowner decided he needed a new road. He suggested to the workmen that they might find the necessary gravel for the road in a bank half a mile from the present shore line, beneath a grove of old birch trees. The men began to dig. They found something even better than gravel—an excellent road surface. They had come upon what seemed to them an ancient oyster bed—though why it should have been inland, they could not imagine.

When Mr. Olsen, the landowner, returned, to see how they were getting on with the digging, one of the men showed him a curiosity. He had found an odd bit of bone among the cockleshells and oyster shells. It looked like a comb with four long teeth.

Olsen looked the comb over carefully. Then he looked into the oyster bed. Among the opened and emptied shells, he saw animal and human bones and other odd bits of worked bone and flint.

Olsen was not an archaeologist, but he was an intelligent man. He realized that the road work had to wait.

Ordering a halt to the digging, Olsen rushed to the Copenhagen Museum to see its director, Jens Worsaae, an old friend. When Worsaae heard the story, he showed Olsen a similar comb, which had been in the museum for a long time. This one was also made of bone.

Now serious digging began on behalf of the museum. A search for similar sites was started, and mounds just like Olsen's—hundreds of them, oyster hills full of man-made artifacts—were discovered all along the old coast line.

"One might be tempted to believe that this had been a sort of eating place for the people of the neighborhood in the earliest prehistoric times. This would account for the ashes, the bones, the flints, and the potsherds," said the museum director.

The mounds soon earned an appropriate name. Since they were the outdoor kitchens of early man, they were called "kitchen middens." *Midden* comes from a Danish word for garbage heap. The discovery, then, turned out to be early man's kitchen garbage.

The great heap formed by the remains of many millions of meals eaten by Stone Age man was like a history book to the scientists. From it archaeologists could tell how Stone Age man had lived; what he ate; what he used as tools and how he made them; what cereals had grown there; what animals he kept.

Today, the site has even been dated quite accurately. The method scientists use is called "carbon dating."

All living matter absorbs carbon. Plants absorb carbon from the air and release oxygen, then the plants are consumed by man and animals. All growing organisms take in new carbon and release old.

Carbon however, comes in three isotopes. Ordinary carbon has an atomic weight of 12 and is called C 12. Heavier carbon is produced in the upper atmosphere, where it has been exposed to bombardment from cosmic rays. When this heavier carbon strikes an atom of carbon in our atmosphere, C 12 changes into C 13 or C 14. This heavy carbon is also absorbed from the atmosphere by all living things.

Since C 14 is radioactive it emits particles which can be measured by a Geiger counter.

Radioactive substances breaking down into other, non-radioactive substances do so at a fixed rate within a fixed time. In other words, the amount of radioactive material is reduced to half within a certain measure of time. After that period it is again reduced to a quarter, and so forth. This fixed rate of disintegration of a radioactive substance is known as its "half-life."

When an organism dies it stops absorbing carbon. Thereafter, its proportion of C 14 to C 12 will slowly drop because of the disintegration process. Scientists have found that the half-life of C 14 is 5,568 years. By counting the clicks on a Geiger counter, scientists can calculate the age of a bone—can tell how long ago it was part of a living animal—and, therefore, when the animal died.

The bone from a dog that was killed 5,568 years ago would produce only half as many clicks on a Geiger counter as a bone that was part of an animal that died yesterday. The bone from a dog that died 11,000 years ago would produce only a quarter as many clicks on the Geiger counter. It would have only a quarter as much C 14 as the dog that died yesterday.

Scientists have now concluded that the eating site on Mr. Olsen's land was used as early as 5000 B.C.

There were dogs in the kitchen midden culture, for dog bones were found there with human bones. We even know the size of the dog—a three-quarter husky. It was a member of man's community seven thousand years ago.

But we can go further back than that.

Let us return again to Star Carr in Yorkshire, England.

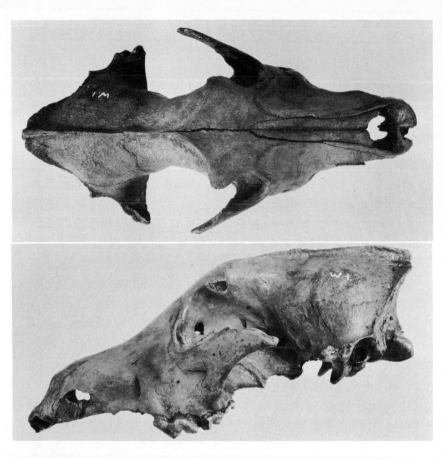

*Two views of the canine cranium found at Star Carr, England—
a prehistoric settlement more than ten thousand years ago*

Five miles south of the fashionable seaside resort of Scarborough, John Moore found, in the summer of 1947, a flint blade in a field-side ditch. When in the following year he found another hillock showing signs of human occupation, Cambridge University archaeologists became interested. They began digging at a nearby site called Star Carr.

Abundant bone remains were sent to the British Museum of Natural History, where they were carefully examined and identified by zoologists F. C. Fraser and Judith King.

By carbon dating, the scientists found that the Star Carr site was even older than the kitchen middens of Denmark. People had eaten here ten thousand years ago. A tibia (a shinbone) from a dog or wolf was among the remains. Later, scientists found part of a dog or wolf skull (they were not sure which it was) and several teeth.

At first, both Drs. Fraser and King suggested that the bone remains were probably an early domesticated dog. But when the book *Excavations at Star Carr* was published, they wrote that the small tibia, together with an incomplete thighbone, and some skull fragments, might better be identified as the bones of a young wolf.

Another view of the skull—1948 excavations

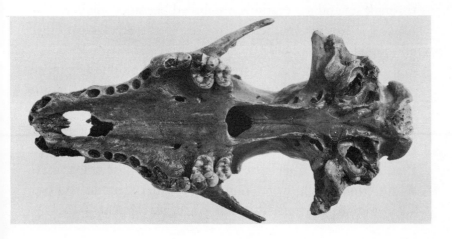

"Two shafts of limb bones have been identified tentatively as *Canis lupus* and may possibly be associated with the juvenile skull fragments. . . . The additional material, in particular the skull of the young wolf, has made it more probable that wolf and not dog is involved," they wrote in their report.

Back at the University of Copenhagen, Dr. Magnus Degerbøl's curiosity was aroused. He had made studies of the remains of dog bones in the peat bogs and kitchen middens of Denmark, and he wondered: perhaps in this early English settlement, this was a very early dog? He wished to pursue the Star Carr investigations further and asked if he might examine the remains. Drs. Fraser and King gladly cooperated, and Dr. Degerbøl set about trying to determine what animal this early Mesolithic find really was: a dog or a wolf.

Scientists know that once a wolf has been domesticated through several generations, the breed becomes smaller. This process accompanies the first phases of the domestication of all animals.

For this reason the scientist compared the bone fragments with those of dogs from early Danish kitchen midden sites and with the bones of prehistoric wolves.

He found the Star Carr jaw much smaller than that of the wolf. He found the tooth-row length in the wolf longer than in the Star Carr specimen. He found that single teeth in the wolf skulls were longer and wider than in the Star Carr animal. Further, the Star Carr jaw appeared to have been weaker than any wolf jaw. Crowding and displacement of teeth is a characteristic feature of the dog. Even in a young wolf skull, the edges of the alveoli, the sockets holding the teeth, are raised above the level of the palate, the roof of the mouth.

Carefully, Degerbøl measured the height of the crown of the left upper canine of the Star Carr animal. It was only 22.2 mm (9/10 of an inch). A young wolf from Langeland in Denmark had a corresponding height of 25.2 mm (or a full inch).

The length of the Star Carr skull was 6¼ inches, compared with 9 inches in the Maalov wolf, 8¼ inches in the Norwegian wolf, and 8 inches in the Greenland dog.

Dr. Degerbøl also found that the Star Carr skull of ten thousand years ago had very large teeth in a very short jaw, with overlapping premolars, and that the teeth of the Star Carr dog were larger than those of the dogs of the later period in Denmark (seven thousand years ago).

This led him to decide that:

1. "The small Star Carr skull cannot be from a wolf, even one kept in captivity for one or two generations, but is clearly from a dog."

2. "If the dog remains from Star Carr are considered as pure dogs with no crossing with wolves, we find that the teeth are so large that they must be of wolf origin."

3. "As the Star Carr dog is a true dog and not a tamed wolf in the first generation of taming, the domestication must have started much earlier than the date of the site."

And so the wild dog, *Canis lupus,* became *Canis familiaris* long before ten thousand years ago, when England was still part of Europe, its shores on the fresh-water Baltic Lake.

Dogs of the early kitchen middens were small. When farming came to Denmark, about 3000 B.C., small dogs were the fashion all over Europe. "The dictate of fashion is the strongest force of nature. In the struggle against wild animals, fairly large and powerful dogs were inevitable—but to give the alarm only, small dogs were just as valuable as large dogs. What we today call large dogs, mastiffs, are not represented in the kitchen middens. Large dogs came to Denmark first in the Iron Age," Dr. Degerbøl wrote.

For an explanation of how man and dog could first have become friends, one must turn to a folk tale—a classic account of how the relationship of man and dog may have begun.

8 ✳

Who Adopted Whom?

In SOUTHERN NIGERIA, among the Africans of Calabar, a story is told which is supposed to show how the wild dog and man first became friends.

Once a boy found a puppy in the forest. Separated from his mother and the other puppies of the litter, the little wild dog was yelping and crying, lost and hungry. The boy gave him a bit of food. The puppy cuddled up to the boy for comfort. The boy carried the dog back to the village.

When the mother dog noticed that her pup was missing, she tried to get him back. Since she was a wild dog who knew enough about men to fear them, she would not approach the village and the glow of its fire. She cried to the puppy; she yowled and howled for his return, but the puppy was happily fed now and would not leave the boy. Again and again the mother came to the edge of the settlement and called to him, but the puppy stayed where he was. Finally the mother gave up and returned to tend to the needs of the rest of her litter.

A St. Bernard carrying a boy on his back

Meanwhile the boy and the puppy became inseparable. The young dog learned about fire, that it was where he could keep warm in the cool evenings, where the food was cooked and eaten, where the scraps were dropped, where his young master sat, where he could crawl beside him and be patted. The puppy became familiar with the camp. As he grew older, he shared in the boy's hunting forays. Afterward, he rested with him, watched over him.

When the dog was full-grown, he lured a young wild female to the fireside. Their puppies, born in the camp, quickly became part of the community. Here was food;

the hunt guaranteed their share. Here also was a pat from a human hand.

Other villages heard about this dog pet who lived with people so happily. They sought out dog pets of their own.

In this way the wild dog became domesticated, entered the home of man, was raised and fed by man's hand.

This folk tale presumes that the boy adopted the dog. Scientists agree that it *could* have happened this way. Pet keeping is one way to domesticate animals, but probably, in the case of the dog, it happened much more casually.

The dog is a natural scavenger. Man and dog were brought together because man was a natural supplier of food. Dog bones in the kitchen middens illustrated this.

Man and dog developed a cooperating relationship, a natural arrangement quite common between other animals.

Dogs hunting for truffles during the Middle Ages

The cowbird, for example, cleans the cow of ticks and fleas. She makes a perch of the cow's wide back, and the cow tolerates the tenant. The cowbird doesn't even bother to build a nest of her own, or to sit on her own eggs. Other birds do that, while she tends to the cow. This is a useful service for the cow, who after all has only a tail to swish away the stinging flies, and no way to scratch out ticks.

The crocodile bird lives on the crocodile's head and bends over to clean the crocodile's teeth after it eats. Fortunately, the crocodile has a thick skin and, like the cow, doesn't mind the passenger perched there. So the crocodile bird has both a protected seat and a sure dinner, while the crocodile has clean teeth.

The hermit crab and the sea anemone are a truly cooperating pair. The crab's shell becomes an apartment for both —the hermit crab lives inside, naturally, and the sea anemone lives on top as a permanent guest in the penthouse. The tentacles of the anemone protect the crab from other animals, while the anemone gets its food from the particles left after the crab has eaten its dinner, besides being carried continuously to new feeding grounds. This is a fairly equal relationship and perhaps most like that which exists between man and dog.

In a cave in the Pyrenees, there is a picture of a great hunt. With man is a wolf, or is it perhaps already a dog?—it is hard to tell. The picture dates from twenty thousand years ago.

Like the wolves, man was a hunter. They were after the

same game. They liked the same food. By accident, they often hunted the same game simultaneously. Soon the wild dog was cooperating.

When the hunt was over and man had had his fill, the wild dogs would turn up as carrion eaters. Once the dog began scavenging within the human group, it became the first animal to be domesticated by man—long before goats or sheep or cattle or horses. These came later, and in just that order. The horse was the last to be domesticated, between about 3000 and 2500 B.C.

The relationship of man and dog developed because the dog is a natural scavenger. The dog turned up, as he had at the kitchen middens, the garbage dumps of ancient times, to find food. The women gathered the oysters. The men brought in the big game. There were scraps enough to share from man's both gathered and hunted meals. And there was still another source of food from man himself.

Man and dog began their relationship because the offal man produces is a delicacy to a dog. It supplies something he likes, in the same way that the salt lick is a treat to a deer.

Long before Star Carr, more than ten thousand years ago, the early dogs kept the hunting sites clean. Their puppies were born in the camps. The dog gave up traveling in packs and turned to man to lead him in the hunt, and accepted his rewards: food and affection.

By Biblical times, the dogs were regarded as "guardians of the house and herd; and scavengers of the streets"—useful

animals—members of man's community performing services to man.

The dog was never domesticated, like cattle, goats, and pigs, for food.

The dog came to man long before man settled down to cultivate the fields, when man was still a hunter, a food gatherer, and they shared their rations and their way of life.

It is obvious, then, that in fact the dog adopted man.

Opposite: *Hunter with Greyhound (Egyptian fresco c. 2800 B.C.)* Below: *Mosaic of a watchdog found in Pompeii*

The children and dogs of Charles I of England
(after a painting by Van Dyck)

66

9 ✳

Dog Sense

THOUGH we say the dog adopted man, it was man who domesticated the dog by feeding him. A fable by Aesop may
demonstrate how:

"A man trained one of his two dogs to hunt and kept the
other as a house dog. The hunting dog complained bitterly
because whenever he caught any game in the chase, the
other was given a share.

" 'It is not fair,' he said, 'that I should go out and have
such a hard time of it, while you do nothing and live well
on the fruits of my labor.'

" 'Well, do not blame me,' said the other dog. 'It is the
master's fault; for he did not teach me to work myself, but
only to eat what others have worked for.' "

The five senses of a dog are the same as the five senses of
man. The dog's sense of taste brought him into man's orbit.
His sense of touch kept him there. The dog liked being
petted.

Fifteenth-century engraving of a hunting dog tracking a scent

His sense of sight is only adequate, though keen at spotting movement. Some see much better than others, but all dogs are color blind and see only gray tones.

Two senses, however, are much more highly developed in the dog than in man: the sense of smell and the sense of hearing.

A dog can detect odors a man does not know exist. A

dog can smell differences between human beings. Most excellent in this ability is the bloodhound, which can pick up the scent of a stranger and follow it for as long as forty-eight hours. As good as any map is a dog's keen nose. In kennel club tests, even ordinary dogs are expected to follow the invisible trail of a human scent for a quarter of a mile, and at its end locate a glove or a wallet having the same scent. Even a piece of wood slightly touched by the master's fingers can be recognized and selected by a dog from among twenty other objects.

"The sense of smell is of the highest importance to the greater number of mammals . . . to the ruminants, in warning them of danger; to the carnivors, in finding their prey . . ." wrote Charles Darwin.

The dog's sense of hearing, too, is much wider and keener than that of man. The silent whistle that trainers use, called the Galton whistle, is pitched so high that the human ear

Greyhound pursuing a hare

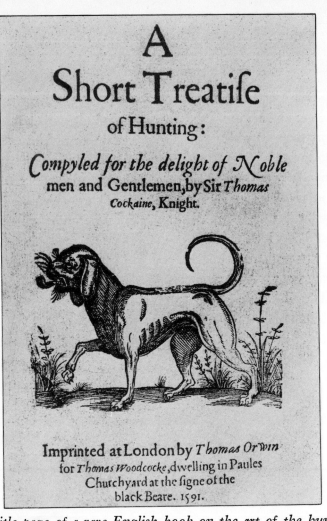

A
Short Treatife
of Hunting:
Compyled for the delight of Noble
men and Gentlemen, by Sir *Thomas*
Cockaine, Knight.

Imprinted at London by *Thomas Orwin*
for *Thomas Woodcocke*, dwelling in Paules
Churchyard at the figne of the
black Beare. 1591.

Title page of a rare English book on the art of the hunt

cannot detect it. A human being cannot catch this sound, does not know it exists, even if he is standing beside the person making it. Yet a dog will respond at more than seventy-five yards. The dog also hears very low tones, far below man's acoustic spectrum.

70

Man has learned to use the dog's senses to warn him of danger, to aid him in hunting, and, of course, to work with him in rescuing the helpless in the Alps.

A dog's simple reflex at the sight of food has also given man a key to understanding some of the ways we learn.

A dog drools at the sight of food. So do other animals, but this reflex is more obvious in the dog. His saliva actually spills over. We also drool, but we express it differently when we see food. We say: "Makes my mouth water."

This curious phenomenon interested a great Russian physiologist who was doing research on how the body as a whole functions. Dr. Ivan Pavlov had already won a Nobel Prize, in 1904, for his work on the circulatory system, but now he set himself the task of finding out why a dog drools.

Dr. Pavlov had chosen dogs as research animals for his study of physiology and had worked with them all his life. He used live animals only and respected the dog above all others. The reason seemed obvious to him. "Dogs," he said, "have been man's best friend since prehistoric times."

Drooling is a reflex, stimulated by the mere sight of food. For his studies Pavlov wanted to measure the quantity of saliva that the dog would drool at the sight of food. He devised a simple way to capture the saliva in a cup and began to make some tests.

He rang a bell. The dog did not drool. Nothing happened. In fact the dog was getting sleepy.

He gave the dog some meat. Of course he drooled. He was wide awake.

Now Pavlov gave the dog some more meat and rang the bell. He repeated this action several times. Soon the dog was drooling every time the bell was rung—even when there was no meat. The dog associated the bell with the food. Dr. Pavlov called this a conditioned response. The animal learned through the act of taking food. By making a connection between the salivary gland and the brain, Pavlov had found a key to learning.

Now he reversed the experiment. He stopped giving the dog food when he rang the bell. Gradually the dog stopped drooling at the sound of the bell. But he continued to do so at the mere sight of food, naturally. Pavlov saw that the dog could also unlearn what he had been taught.

This is one way all animals learn, including the human ones. We, too, are conditioned by the way we get our food.

Once the dog depended on man for food, he learned from man, and man became his teacher and master.

We have seen that the dog entered the human creature's community voluntarily, first as a scavenger. He found the pickings good and remained to join with man on his hunting trips. He cooperated with the hunter to obtain food, and when man settled down and domesticated new animals, the dog once again became part of man's changing world, adapting to his changing needs.

The second animal man domesticated was the goat; later, the sheep. These animals not only provided meat without hunting—but goats and sheep gave milk, hides, skins, hair, wool, and fat.

Man now had herds to watch over. He became a shepherd with a flock, and his dogs became his helpers. There were several different kinds and sizes of dog, each with a different function to perform. While the shepherd was away from home, his property and family needed guarding. Dogs were soon bred as warning dogs. While the women were weaving the wool into garments or making cheese from the milk, little house dogs could quickly warn with a bark that a stranger approached the door. Soon there would be bigger protectors.

The sheep dog, used in the fields, was moderately large during the Bronze Age, and very like some still to be found in parts of Europe. Sheep dogs were not used for hunting. Instead, they kept the flock together, rounded up stragglers, and guided them back to the grazing grounds. Then they led the way home or to watering sites, obeying the orders of the master, the shepherd.

The sheep dog's sense of herding was a holdover from his days as a hunter. His sharp sense of smell could locate any missing animal.

Then there was the great shepherd dog. He was the shepherd's home sentinel, trained to protect. Even his size inspired fear. He could control a man. If he were tied up, he guarded the home and warned of any who came near. Otherwise, allowed to roam the village freely, he scavenged in the streets, nosing into debris of all sorts.

It is from these mastiffs, the shepherd dogs, that the St. Bernard is descended. But though he is strong and powerful,

An engraving after Edwin Landseer's "Alpine Mastiffs Reanimating a Traveller." The wine keg hanging from the collar of the St. Bernard on the left was an invention of the artist's; wine kegs have never been carried by the Hospice dogs.

he does not behave like a shepherd dog, a guard. The St. Bernard acts like a sheep dog, leading his human flock to safety.

On August 29, 1867, Henri Schumacher de Hollingen wrote to the Reverend Macdona of England, explaining how the rescue work at the St. Bernard Pass was conducted. "Each morning two dogs, an old one and a young one, take the road on the Italian side of the mountain to Aosta. Two others take the road on the Swiss side to Martigny. On both routes various stone shelters have been built for refuge of travelers surprised by snow. . . . Both teams go as far as the last shelter on either side. Even if it snowed the previous night, the dogs never fail to find the route, which means that travelers on the way to the Hospice can follow their tracks."

Schumacher explained that two dogs go in case of accident, a young and an old one—the young one to learn. If the dogs find someone in the shelter they try to entice the travelers to follow them to the Hospice. If they cannot do so, they return to the Hospice and lead the monks back, who then administer first aid.

Schumacher described the training as though the dogs were trained only by each other and set out like sheep dogs to bring the stragglers home.

But the St. Bernard has *not* learned to do this alone. Man has taught him.

IO ✳

Is the Bark Learned?

THEY SAY wolves only howl, while dogs bark. But is this true?

The word "dog" in English was derived from the sound of a bark from a distance: "daw daw daw daw." Dog was the name of a particular breed in England long ago that made this sound. The word now applies to all domesticated dogs in the English language.

But there are dogs that do not bark.

An early book on English dogs lists one. Written in 1576, when Elizabeth I was queen, by Johannes Caius (Keyes), a professor at the University of Cambridge, it spoke of a special dog without a bark. Poachers used the breed to hunt in the queen's forest, and it earned the name, "thievish dog." The breed no longer exists in the British Isles, and there is no way to check if it was really mute or whether it had been made voiceless by the poachers themselves.

The Basenji of Africa is also known as a barkless dog.

The most insulting thing one can call a person in the

Congo is "Basenji." The name was given the little dogs in error by white explorers who asked its name and were told the dog belonged to the Basenji—"people of the bush" (our equivalent word would be "backwoodsmen")—and so they assumed that the name of the *dog* was Basenji. The natives call it the "jumping-up-and-down-dog," since it leaps high to try to see over the tall elephant grass.

Dr. John Paul Scott, who has studied the social behavior of the dog, and who has experimented with the Basenji, says that the dogs bark "rarely." He also believes that this rarely used bark is an evolved trait. That is, the Basenji, once a barking dog, has been selected for its non-barking trait, by

A Basenji

staying alive. "In the African forests, leopards are reputedly fond of dog meat, and it may be that the dog which barks simply attracts attention to himself and comes to an untimely end," Dr. Scott says.

Basenjis do "crow, yowl and howl." Dr. Scott suggests that Basenjis have developed sounds with "unusual acoustic qualities." He believes that the Basenji barklessness is a "protective function" which safeguards the breed against the threats of death in the forests of Africa.

When raised in a kennel with other dogs, even Basenjis will become barkers. However, they bark only about a fifth as much as other breeds, and it seems to the casual observer that by comparison, Basenjis are strangely silent.

There are other non-barking dogs.

The sixteenth-century Spanish explorer Juan Fernandez

*A team of
Eskimo dogs
in the 1800s*

described three native dogs he found in Mexico and wrote
that some were dumb and barkless.

Dr. Magnus Degerbøl has said of Eskimo dogs: "For
years, I had here in Denmark a pure Greenland dog from
Angmagssalik, East Greenland. Generally Eskimo dogs do
not bark. The first time my Greenland dog barked was
when he was three-quarters of a year old. It happened one
day as a few ants walked right against it, and the poor creature was so astonished that it said: 'wow,' and once again,
'wow.' Later, when it became an adult, it barked very rarely
and always when it was surprised or excited."

Zoo keepers noticed that in captivity the wolf barks. Some
believed this was learned.

E. Kuyt, the Canadian biologist, heard wolves, whether
wild or captive, bark "on occasion. It is not as pronounced

as a dog's bark, but more like a coughlike 'woof,' " he said. "I have heard only the male bark and always when it was surprised."

In *White Fang* Jack London expresses starkly how a seemingly barkless wolf attempts to get help for his injured master. In the story the adopted wolf has only once before made a short, startled bark, to warn his master of danger. It, too, was a single "woof." But now his master is in deep trouble, and help is needed immediately. He runs to his master's home:

"White Fang turned to the love-master's wife. She screamed with fright as he seized her dress in his teeth and dragged on it till the frail fabric tore away. By this time he had become the center of interest. He had ceased his growling and stood, head up, looking into their faces. His throat worked spasmodically, but made no sound, while he struggled with all his body, convulsed with the effort to rid himself of the incommunicable something that strained for utterance. . . . At this moment speech came to White Fang, rushing up in a great burst of barking.

"They were all on their feet, now, and White Fang ran down the steps, looking back for them to follow. For the second and last time in his life he had barked and made himself understood."

Adolph Murie reports that wolves both bark and howl. He heard them. While searching for the wolf den and the newborn puppies, Murie heard a wolf howl. Later he saw a black wolf on the run. A half-mile away, the wolf stopped to bark. In this way Murie knew he had located the den with the puppies. He was close to the lair. In fact, Murie shortly heard both adults bark "sometimes in a series, and ending in a long howl."

The bark is an alarm signal when some stranger invades the wolf den or territory.

The howl is the way the wolves keep in touch with the pack while hunting miles away from home.

Since few persons do in fact invade the wolf den, all they ever hear are their distant howls.

The St. Bernard dog barks, but rarely. It also yowls and howls like a wolf. But mostly it is silent. Perhaps, as with the Basenji, this trait evolved due to selection.

Perhaps the Basenji, which did not bark, has survived because the leopards could not locate him. Though there are no leopards in the great white world of the mountains, there are tons of movable snow. These can be triggered into motion by sound. The barking of a dog can set a slide roaring down a mountain side. Perhaps for this reason the St. Bernards work silently.

When they are in their kennel playground, their movements are swift and agile—they seem to swim over the snow—but there is no barking. When they are at rest in their kennel cages, they are relaxed, sleepy-eyed, at peace. They greet you with a wag of the tail—but no bark.

The bark is used to signal that they have found someone in the snow—one bark, deep and throat-wrenching.

II ✳

The Breed

Five Swiss dogs of today are believed to have come with the Romans two thousand years ago. The St. Bernard, the largest, the most imposing, and the most famous of the five, has earned itself the popular title of Swiss National Dog.

The other dogs are: the Great Swiss Mountain Dog, the Bernese Mountain Dog, the Appenzell Mountain Dog, and the Entlebuch Mountain Dog—all named for the mountainous areas where they developed and made their homes.

None of the four had names until about sixty years ago. They were just farm dogs. The owners told fantastic stories about their abilities and performances. The dogs seemed to have been there always, and they were kept on for their usefulness.

The coloring of all four is similar: a black coat, white toes, white tail point, white breast, and a white line between the eyes toward the nose. Between the white and the black on the feet there is also some brown, as on both sides of the white breast. A brown spot on the nose, brown tips just above the eyes, and falling ears are also common.

Above Right: *An Entlebuch Mountain Dog*
Above Left: *A Great Swiss Mountain Dog*
Below: *A Bernese Mountain Dog*

The Great Swiss is the tallest of the four; he has short hair and a falling tail, and resides in the countryside of central Switzerland, of which the capital city, Berne, is the heart. This area is called the Bernese Midlands. The Great Swiss is considered to be one of the great-grandparents of the St. Bernard.

Next in size is the sturdier Bernese Mountain Dog, with shorter legs and long hair. Of the four types, the Bernese Mountain Dog is the most popular, the typical house dog of the Bernese farmer. The home of this breed is in the mountain region of Durbach Graben. In the Berne countryside this sturdy dog was used as a draft animal. He pulled the little carts filled with woven baskets to market and helped with the products of the cheese farms.

The Appenzell Mountain Dog is the liveliest of the group, having what dog owners call a "great temperament." It is used as a house dog and on the farm as a herder. It works with tremendous energy and great pleasure.

The Entlebuch Mountain Dog is the smallest of the four. It, too, is a herder and watchdog.

An Appenzell Mountain Dog

In Roman times, the large dogs were used as warrior dogs or guard dogs on sentry duty with the soldiers. The smaller dogs helped to transport the supply herds over the Alps. An unfriendly people would certainly not feed an invading army, so the Romans brought their own cattle and sheep dogs along. When the soldiers were forced back to the south, their dogs remained in isolated mountain valleys and peaks, and the strains continued.

The monks of the Great St. Bernard Pass began systematically breeding their dogs, still called Barry dogs at the time, only about 1665. In the St. Bernard the black color of the Great Swiss and the Roman Molosser was bred out.

Old Swiss and German scrolls of the fourteenth century depicted a large mastiff, similar to the modern St. Bernard. And there is a painting of William Tell, the great fifteenth-century Swiss patriot, showing him posed with two large white dogs which look somewhat like white St. Bernards.

The very first time the dogs were described as St. Bernard dogs, as a special breed, was by Eberhard August Wilhelm von Zimmerman in *The Geographical History of Man and the Four-Footed Animals*, published in Leipzig in 1778–80.

At only one point, and as late as 1830, did the monks cross a St. Bernard with another breed of dog—the Newfoundland. Since the Newfoundland was such a strong retriever, they hoped to inbreed the instinctive retrieving trait. The Newfoundland is a long-haired dog, and as a result a long-haired variety of the St. Bernard was developed.

Some of the brothers thought that long hair might be an

advantage to the dog in the bitter cold at the Pass. But the reverse proved to be true. The long hair handicapped the dog. Ice crystals and snowballs collected and matted hair and paws, impeding the dog's work.

The long-haired puppies thereafter were sent down to the valley as watchdogs and sheep dogs, and the short-haired variety was kept in the mountains. In this way two strains of St. Bernard were developed: a short- and long-haired, both authentic St. Bernard dogs.

In 1855 the first breeding kennel outside of the Hospice was formed in Berne by Henri Schumacher de Hollingen. He began breeding with a single male dog purchased from Count Rougemont. This dog was short-haired; his grandmother had come from the Hospice twenty years before. Continuing to breed his dogs with dogs from the Hospice, Henri Schumacher began to export St. Bernards all over the world. They were particularly popular in England and Russia on large estates, where they proved to be not only excellent watchdogs but also good, gentle house dogs and companions for children.

The St. Bernard Club of Switzerland was organized in 1884, and at Zurich in 1877 the Swiss characteristics rather than the English were officially recognized.

The Hospice as a breeding kennel also belongs to the St. Bernard Club of Switzerland. Now all dogs at the Great St. Bernard Pass have a pedigree and are registered with the Swiss St. Bernard Club.

12 ✳

A Tragedy

THERE WAS an end and a new beginning to the work of the dogs at the top of the world.

The end came in tragedy, as the world charged headlong into war.

Over the years, the need for the dog and the monk as guides over the Pass had lessened. The footpath of Strabo's time was only a bridle path in Napoleon's day. But in 1885 telegraph came to the Pass. Travelers could be warned of snow conditions on the mountains before they began their journey. In 1906 the Simplon was pierced by a tunnel through the mountains, affording a safer way to travel than the dangerous one across the summit.

After 1918, travelers rarely walked over the Great St. Bernard Pass, and certainly not in bad weather. The monks and their dogs no longer met the travelers in the cave at Bourg-St. Pierre, though they continued to make their rounds over the mountain passes, morning and evening.

After the sport of skiing became popular, the work of the

dogs became almost useless. The dogs, who had been success-
ful in finding footpaths under the snow by means of their
acute sense of smell, were no longer a necessity. At least so it
seemed. A skier did not need a footpath. With skis a man
could almost fly down the hillside, gliding over the snow,
cutting across paths and ravines.

A long-haired St. Bernard

The big dogs could not keep up with a skier. They were too slow. It took only half an hour to glide down the mountains where, before skis, it took four or five hours to walk.

The monks and their dogs continued working together. They were always ready for emergencies. But their day-in and day-out vigil was relaxed. As time went on, the dogs were used only occasionally, in blinding fog, or in the event of a great accident. The program that had inspired the world, and become a model for all other programs, had apparently come to an end.

Two years before World War II, in 1937, a shocking tragedy occurred at the Pass.

The pack of St. Bernards, allowed to run free as they always had—trusted implicitly—somehow pounced upon a twelve-year-old girl, Marianne Brémond, who had run to greet them. She was so badly hurt that she died.

No one knows how it happened. There were no witnesses. Why had the gentle dogs suddenly acted like ferocious wolves? Had the child fought them? So had the boy Martin, who had stabbed and wounded Barry. Was it because the dogs were in a pack? They always went on their morning runs together, unleashed and free, easily controlled with a call.

The dogs themselves could give no answers.

The breed was on trial for its life. A little girl was dead.

A grief-stricken parent, Dr. Brémond, demanded that the state of Valais order a halt to the raising of St. Bernard dogs. There was an inquiry. The Hospice was ordered to kill all the old dogs involved in the incident and to no longer permit the dogs to roam as an unsupervised pack.

However, after carefully investigating all the facts, the commander of the Gendarmes Gollut decided that the demand to discontinue the breed was excessive.

The dogs, as a breed, could continue.

Soon Europe itself erupted into violence and the Second World War began. The passes were closed. The military guarded all comings and goings at the St. Bernard.

Later, with peace, there would be more motor ways and more tunnels through the mountains, even one at the Great St. Bernard, a few miles below the Hospice itself.

In the years between the tragedy and the opening of the new cut through the great rock, the monks continued to breed their dogs, they continued to work quietly with them.

The long-haired puppies were still sent to the valleys and the farms around; the short-haired dogs stayed in the mountains with the monks or at Martigny, twenty-four miles away, their winter quarters below. The monks continued to exercise, train, play with them in the snow. How the dogs enjoyed pulling the toboggans and chasing the monks on their skis!

The dogs and the monks were not to be separated. But at the time the question of how they were to serve in the future was left unanswered. There were still avalanches in the mountains—and there were many more thousands of skiers. There was still much work to be done—as any present-day visitor to the Pass realizes.

13 ✳

First View of the Alps

WHEN THE SWALLOWS pass over the Great St. Bernard in
their semiannual migrations to and from Europe, they pause
at the Hospice. Exhausted from traveling at high altitudes,
they fly right into the windows, left open in welcome. They
will not take food, but they do stop and rest before flying
on—as so many voyagers have done over the centuries.

The tiny Dauphine car, which Gisela Quitzau, my friend
and photographer, and I used, negotiated the hairpin turns,
climbing higher and higher at each wild curve while the
precipice always beckoned directly below. The car was a
great mountain climber, but often there just did not seem
time enough to change from one to another of its four gears.

Here, the road was heavily traveled. For it was vacation
time, and holidayers were everywhere. There was a hustle
and bustle of people on the route through the Pass, traveling
in buses and supply trucks, on motor bikes; cyclists, hikers,
walkers, people with their skis packed on the top of their
cars. On the mountain, there might be snow.

All of us had left the wider, safer road leading into the tunnel, which by-passed the summit and cut through to Italy. Officially opened on March 19, 1964, after five long years of work, it diverted most of the heavy traffic. Only visitors ventured to the summit.

When we started out from Geneva it had been sunny. We drove through summer, along the southern shore of the great lake, up into the mountains of winter.

At the top, its tiny lake was obscured with mist, like a steamy coffee cup freshly filled.

We were high over Europe with our heads in the clouds, and clouds below our neck, blowing by. The misty air was penetratingly damp, cold, and gray.

Even as we parked beside the Hospice we could see the sign *Chenil* pointing up into more clouds, where the dog kennel was. We were too cold to pay a visit then. But before we entered the Hospice, we looked for one brief moment at the peaks all around—arms into the sky—an awesome place.

It was July 8, but who would know it was summer?

Yet when we looked closer to the earth, we could see tiny daisies abloom, the size of buttercups back home. Violets thrived beside the snow, large as African violets with bright yellow centers. Here, yarrow was as dainty as baby's breath, and forget-me-nots, unforgettably large. Botanists have identified twelve hundred different kinds of flowers at the Pass. The plants have adjusted to the climate in many ways, and

Canon and young dogs at the Hospice

bloom next to patches of snow—bright spots among the mosses and lichens and tough grass. Under a rock on a high bluff, where only the hardiest could venture, was the edelweiss, noble white.

Our teeth were chattering with cold as we opened the Hospice door. The whole place buzzed with young life—hostelers who had spent the night, visiting students, people who had come from Austria, Italy, France, and Scandinavia just to see the dogs.

We did not know where to turn or with whom to talk. A young priest opened the door to the kitchen. Warm air rushed into the cold hall. Young, smiling, red-cheeked, cheerful, the priest greeted us and asked us to come in. Quickly, he offered us seats in the warm kitchen and set about making tea. We were travelers, too, and first we needed to be fed. But he did not stay with us long

"Père Econome!" someone called.

The priest answered and disappeared. He ran out to help with this or to see to that. He was obviously in charge of all economy and management.

By the time he returned the water had boiled. He poured it into a pot and set out the cups. Then he gave each of us a warming cupful. Soon our teeth stopped chattering. We then explained the purpose of our visit. We had come, like the children, to see the dogs, but we also hoped to do a book about them. We hoped to get his help.

"Père Econome!" someone else called, and he dashed off again.

But soon he returned with another St. Augustine Father to join in our tea. The Father was happy to talk with us and tell us about the new role of the St. Bernard dogs.

"Will the work of the St. Bernards continue?" we asked.

"Yes, but in a different way," he explained. "There will always be St. Bernards at the Pass. We raise them here and at Martigny and sell them. However, each year we train one or two dogs for avalanche work."

At my next question, the Father smiled. "Did the dogs carry wine in barrels?" He admitted that the story was more legend than fact. "What is important is the rucksack that the master carries, for the necessary things for rescue work."

Later we learned that the legend of the little kegs began in England, with the arrival there in 1815 of Lion. A thirteen-year-old boy, son of an artist, was so moved by the story of the majestic dog that he drew a St. Bernard, and his brother made an engraving of it. This boy later became Sir Edwin Henry Landseer and played with the rescue theme many times. In 1820 he painted an Alpine mastiff reanimating a traveler, and in 1831 John Landseer made another famous and popular engraving. It was the Landseers' imaginative play with the famous dogs that made them invent the little wooden wine casks to carry around their necks. It did not occur at the Pass.

In windless weather the St. Bernard can pick up the scent of a human at a distance of more than eight hundred feet and in the face of a wind at a distance of several miles. An avalanche dog must trace the scent of people buried five to seven feet deep in the snow.

The St. Augustine Father said: "Their sense of smell is *très très*, very good; different, not like a bloodhound's, but as good."

The two things that the Father was most proud of were: "their strength and their lightness in the snow.

"They have a skin between their toes, so that their large paws are like natural snowshoes. Their feet have a web almost like a duck's, and this makes them specially good for avalanche work. They can run and walk in the snow without sinking in."

Snowshoe feet?

This we had to see for ourselves.

But it was evening now, and we would have to wait until morning.

Our interview had to end, since the Father was due to go to the Hospice at the Simplon Pass for several days. There were also a kennel and rescue dogs there.

But the Father promised us help. "Père Econome will be your guide," he said.

After gracious farewells he left to join the other, younger priests and seminarians in prayer. They filed by through the narrow hallway to the church, moving like a long line of skiers.

It was arranged. At 4 A.M. the next morning we were to join Paul Vuyet, the dogs' trainer and attendant, when he took them on their three-hour morning run through the mountains.

14 ✳

Snowshoe Feet

BEFORE WE WENT to bed that night, we decided to try the famous St. Bernard brandy, produced from honey the bees made from the nectar of flowers on the mountain.

Across the road from the Hospice was a hotel. At the rear of the restaurant, where we could get the brandy, there was a fire in a small stove. It gave out little warmth and was already surrounded by visitors who were not used to this Alpine "summer." So we sat between too drafty doors and tried to warm ourselves with the brandy. It was sweet and tasty. We sipped it slowly.

Later, we had a leisurely dinner, and went to bed early. We had had a long day, and tomorrow would be even longer. We had to be up before 4 A.M.

Getting ready for bed was simple. We took no clothes off, we just put more on. Two suits, two sweaters—and even with these we shivered at the thought of the cold, pure white linen sheets that covered the beds. The eiderdown covers felt splendidly soft, but we had little confidence that they would warm us. Icicles still hung from the eaves outside our window.

When we finally crawled in, there was a surprise at the foot of our beds. Someone had given each of us a hot water bottle to warm our toes. Soon we would be cozy enough to doze, we thought.

But time passed, and sleep did not come. Gisela must have fallen asleep, since she did not stir. But I lay awake, warm, not even drowsy, completely alert. Nothing would make me sleep. Counting sheep, remembering numbers, pleasant things . . . nothing worked. Meanwhile the alarm clock given us ticked like a steady gong at every second. Somehow the hours went by.

From the kennel a great cacophony of sound arose. The dogs were howling and yowling like wolves—eerie and frightening. Obviously, it must be time to get up; the dogs were calling to be let out.

The alarm never had to go off. I got up to look at the clock and saw that it was time: nearly 4 A.M. And I had slept not one wink.

Gisela was stirring, too.

"Did you sleep?" I asked.

"Not one moment," she said.

We both laughed.

Afraid of disturbing me, she had been silent, just as I had for her sake.

"It must have been the brandy," I suggested. "We must ask Paul when we see him if it is really so strong."

Trainer Paul Vuyet with two of his St. Bernards

We added even more clothes to those we still wore: two pairs of socks, over stockings, and all the suits and sweaters we had brought with us. Gisela had forgotten her slacks, and since she would have to jump around taking photographs, I gave her mine. Over the suits, I put on a wool coat, a scarf, even long white gloves. All I wanted was to be warm. I didn't care how silly I looked.

Right on time, we walked up to the *chenil* and waited for Paul. We were afraid to go any farther, for the dogs were continuing their concert. As we approached the kennel they stopped. But as soon as they heard footsteps coming toward them, they began to yowl and howl again. We waited where we were, below the entrance.

Surely if Paul was already inside he would open the door for us or call out. He would know by the sounds the dogs were making that strangers had approached. So we waited, the wind howling around us, wet and cold, the dogs howling inside.

Then the dogs settled down. They were silent, too, waiting.

Gisela's hands were so cold that she was afraid she wouldn't be able to press the trigger on her camera. Shivering just from standing, I decided to return to the Hospice and look for Paul.

But all was silent there. Not a soul stirred. Church services did not start until 6 A.M. I couldn't go knocking on doors to waken Père Econome. I returned to the kennel thinking perhaps there was another route that Paul had followed to a rear door. It was so quiet inside suddenly that Gisela and I started expectantly up the stairs.

The howling and yowling began again. No, we shouldn't go inside alone. With the bitter, wet wind swirling around me, once more I walked down the hill to the Hospice. Obviously, no one had believed we would be up and ready by 4 A.M. Paul appeared at the door, rubbing the sleep out of his eyes. Somehow he had overslept. "Have you had breakfast?" I asked. Gisela and I had already managed to get a cup of coffee at the restaurant.

"Oh, no," he answered, "I go with them on an empty stomach." Then he asked how we had slept.

"Not at all," I said. "We sipped a thimbleful of your famous St. Bernard brandy and we never got to sleep. Is it a stimulant?"

He laughed. "Yes, it is the brandy made of honey and herbs of the mountains, to give to people in the snow. It gives them strength to walk!"

"Then we should have walked last night. Now we are tired from lack of sleep," I laughed.

By this time we were at the steps where Gisela had waited for us. We started to follow Paul up the stairs, feeling brave enough beside him, but he wanted to go in alone. So we waited. Inside, there was a stillness of anticipation.

Suddenly the kennel doors opened onto the playground with its high ten-foot fence. The dogs came out leaping into the enclosed yard, charged with energy, circling each other, sniffing, smelling, tumbling about, glad to be free at last.

They ran up to the high gate where we were standing, and for a moment I remembered that small girl and the tragedy. But Paul was right there with the dogs, talking to them, calling them by name. He opened the gates, and they ran toward us, all together, friendly and expecting attention. We patted them on their heads as they went by us—twenty dogs as large as lions. I was frightened even of their friendliness. But it was freedom that they wanted, and off they ran.

They led us up the path to the higher mountain. We passed the chair lift which crosses over the great valley to the next peak, from which one can see Mont Blanc in France. We were following the dogs. They stopped to investigate something, then they were following us. They kept up a loping, back-and-forth run—much like cantering. They loved the patches of snow, they ate of it, and rolled in it. And there was always some new and strange pleasure to explore, to sniff at, dog fashion. Yet never were they far from Paul's voice.

When they seemed to wander too far, his single call brought them back. He called them by their names. If two dogs seemed too playful, too frisky, Paul spoke sharply, and they would come to him. He knew each one, and they knew their own names. They would obey immediately, pause to be petted, then run off again.

"My dogs are like children," Paul said. "I can take all twenty of them on a walk and control them with a word, a

The dogs await their morning run.

personal call, by their personal name. That is all the command they need."

The path was getting steeper and steeper as we circled the mountain peak. After our sleepless night and our long wait in the cold, we were exhausted. We couldn't continue the three-hour walk. And the camera wasn't working. Gisela's hands were chilled numb. So we excused ourselves to Paul, and said we would meet him on the way down, after we had warmed up again. In the meantime, we would return to the hotel for breakfast.

Paul started up the path, but one large dog waited, wanting an embrace. He stood up beside Paul, matching him shoulder

Trainer Vuyet and friend, before the morning run

to shoulder and head to head, to the height of six feet. The dog was more massive than the man, stronger and heavier. Then he sat down on his haunches—his face the solemn mask of benevolence that is the St. Bernard insignia. He lifted his paw for me to shake.

This was the moment to see if there really was skin like a duck's between the toes.

I took the large paw in my hands. It overflowed my fingers and my palm. There were the four toes without the extra undeveloped dew claw. With Paul's help I separated each of the four toes to see for myself if the space between was even slightly webbed.

There, between each toe, was a webbing of skin which came down a quarter of the toe length.

The Tibetan mastiff also frequently had such a skin between its toes. So did the Newfoundland, with which the St. Bernard was intentionally bred during the last century and might more likely be the source of this useful characteristic.

Combined with the enormity of their paws, the webbing helps make the St. Bernards gifted workers in the snow. They do possess nature's own snowshoes.

15 ✴

Puppytime at the Pass

SUMMERTIME is puppytime at the St. Bernard Pass.

Everyone who comes has come to see the dogs—but the puppies, of course, steal the show.

The holiday spirit is everywhere. The children are dressed for warmer vacation weather, with sandals and socks, short skirts and shorter shorts, a simple stretch of shirt or blouse; their naked knees knock with the cold, and they all look a bit blue as they await their turn to go through the kennel.

But they are not thinking of their comfort now. The excitement warms them. Later, they may have a snack or dinner at the hotel, and drive down the mountain to wherever they were going in the first place, laden with souvenirs: cowbells, charms for the neck, stuffed dogs carrying the legendary small wooden barrel, a bottle of St. Bernard brandy, or an embroidered emblem, the modern day insignia of the Pass, to sew on their jackets.

Some may stop just long enough to write a postcard, for it will bear the special stamp of the St. Bernard Pass.

There are buses full of teen-agers, a caravan of climbers, skiers—for here there is still a patch of snow—families rushing up to the kennel: as many as one thousand visitors on a single Sunday during the short Alpine summer.

The kennel is a long, low shed on a flat lip cut from the rock. One must climb a sharp incline, pocked and rutted by the rush of waters, then walk up two flights of stairs to the corridor where the dogs are now at rest, some sleeping.

The large dogs fill up the space allotted them almost completely, like lions poured into cages. Sometimes one

St. Bernard pups on the steps of the Hospice

will open an eye, a very red eye, and look at you; but mostly they rest. They are tired because they have already run for three hours in the snow, where they rolled and chased and sped as fast as they cared to go around the familiar path. They look bored. Sometimes one opens a large black mouth and yawns. Solemn dogs.

As one benevolent giant yawned in my face and looked at me out of bloodshot eyes, Paul explained: "From the snow."

The dogs have been Paul's responsibility for the last ten years. Now he has a fourteen-year-old helper, a printer's apprentice from Sion, Italy, named Pierre André Duc who has come up for the summer to work. Every year Paul brings a young lad to the mountains as a helper.

The monks of the St. Bernard Pass are responsible for the *dressage*, the training of the dogs for avalanche duty, but Paul and his helper tend to the chores of the kennel. Paul, alone, takes them on their three-hour run over the mountains at 4 A.M. He feeds them and plays with them in their run, or playground, or *parc*, as it is variously called. He sees to the visitors and even collects the fees as people pour through the door. Paul can make change like a bank, for the fees are paid in as many different currencies as there are visitors from foreign countries.

Pierre André Duc understands only Italian, but he, too, has learned to make change in any kind of coin. Today he is cashier, there are so many guests.

Pierre had been here the summer before, when he was

helper to the helper, his older brother. This year he is an official apprentice. It is his first summer actually working with the dogs.

"And who is your favorite?" I asked him.

"But of course, Bari," he answered.

The dogs' names are formally posted on cards over their doors. When you talk with them, you may address them properly: Neptune, Bello, Nora, Fiora, Roy, Alfa, Almira, Bianca, Rigo, Aslo, Bella, Amidor, Gini, Ella, Fiana, and Bari.

Ella, the mother of four puppies when we saw her, worked the year before for twelve hours in a snowstorm at the Simplon Pass, on avalanche rescue. In July her puppies were already gawky pre-adolescents. They filled up the whole cage and at three months were losing their chubby roundness.

St. Bernards are prolific breeders. They can have between three and seventeen puppies in a litter, but ten is about average. However, the breeders have found that the mother can properly take care of only six, so it is the rule of the St. Bernard Society that the mother raises only six of her litter.

At birth, a puppy will weigh just under a pound. It gains twenty to twenty-five pounds a month in the first few months of its development—a very fast-growing animal. Then it slows down, reaching full growth at two years.

At the Pass, the routine for puppy care is Paul's responsibility. Paul immediately takes them away from the mother

Mother dog nursing her four-week-old puppies

at birth. He keeps them under a warming lamp, returning them to her for nursing every two hours. This is done because the mother is so heavy and clumsy in a confined area that she might accidentally crush the pups.

This routine goes on for eighteen days, until the puppy's eyes are open and it can move about on its sturdier legs. After that, the puppy stays with the mother all the time.

Young puppies are given bottled mother's milk for supplemental feedings. Then they get cow's milk to lap on their own. Later, they will eat polenta, a kind of corn cereal, once a day. A full-grown dog will eat about a pound of polenta, cooked in fat, and more than a pound of meat each day—the combined food making a kilo to a kilo and a half (2.2 to 3.3 pounds) of food.

The puppies will eat three times a day. Dogs from six months to a year will eat twice a day, and the adults are served only once.

From the very first, the young St. Bernard becomes attached to his human handler. The puppies at the Pass are friendly, energetic, happy to extend a paw for anyone to shake. They naturally retrieve; throw them something and they will bring it right back.

"How do you choose which puppies to keep?" I asked.

Paul answered: "Just at random. Not by the markings—they are all so pretty, it is hard to choose. I have to close my eyes and pick."

But Père Econome explained the selection differently. "At birth, we eliminate the subjects which are not all of the race; for example, the dogs that are too white. We select them after they are ten days old, since there is some loss of life in the first six weeks after birth. We keep four males and two females."

At three to four months the puppies begin to eat meat—finely chopped. This is both beef and horsemeat. Now they start to work with their master for an hour a day, so that a psychological attachment develops. The rigorous *dressage* does not begin until seventeen months. Training an avalanche dog takes two and a half years in all.

Since only two dogs a year are trained, the others are sold. Puppies with a pedigree can be bought from the Hospice at two and a half months for about two hundred dollars apiece.

Two trained dogs and a few monks remain at the Hospice through the long winter. The others go down to the winter kennels at Martigny, twenty-four miles away and marked by a milepost from Roman days. Here the long and arduous training in avalanche rescue is given.

But the summertime, at the Pass, is devoted to the visitors.

As guests poured through the door, they read the dogs' names aloud. They talked to them. Sometimes they were able to rouse the dogs sufficiently to make them stand up and shake hands. The kennel is strangely quiet for the number of dogs in it—there is no yapping, yelping, or barking now.

Bari is there. He is the young male who gives promise of being a great avalanche rescuer. He is now in the midst of his training. He is not the largest dog, but they are sure that he will do honor to the name. He is quick to learn.

The other dog being trained at this time is Fiana. By September she will be ready to engage in rescue work. At two and a half years of age she will begin her true function at the Pass.

Most of the visitors stop longest in front of the cage with four puppies. Their gawky, clumsy legs, their rolling gait,

are engaging. Their facial expressions are sweet, full of won-
der and curiosity.

Pierre picked up a puppy for us to hold. It was a heavy
armful. We had to support its legs because they seemed to
want to drop off with their own weight. Those legs were
meant to support a strong body on the ground, not to dangle
dangerously in mid-air.

The puppy was glad to be put back into the cage with
its brothers, and they all tumbled about in welcome.

16 ✳

Snow Training

PÈRE ECONOME, who had been the first to greet us and serve us the warming cup of tea, spoke in detail about the training of the dogs.

Sitting in the rectory of the Hospice, at a long table under a high, wide window that opened onto the vast panorama of the mountains, we could talk and watch a group of skiers slaloming down to the edge of the lake. There was still enough snow for them—and this morning there was sunshine, too.

Père Econome explained that since 1963 the work of the St. Bernard dogs has been incorporated into an over-all Alpine rescue program for avalanche accidents.

In the training of the dogs for this work, there are three classes: Debutante, Middle, and Elite.

The first part of the program begins when the dogs are about seventeen months old, in a concentrated two-week course. But it really starts with the development of a strong attachment between dog and master, always a priest who is also skilled in skiing and other arts needed in snow rescue.

Master and dog have already developed a relationship since puppyhood, when at three or four months the dog begins eating small pieces of meat from his master's hand. But now the real work begins. The dog is almost fully matured. His attachment to his master has been achieved through work and exercise, feeding, demonstrations of affection—through daily contact.

Now the dog's first task is to learn to look for his master. He must develop discipline through constant close exercise with his trainer.

If the dog exercises well, the Father gives him a bit of meat. He caresses the dog, praises him. Petting is an important part of the development of the relationship between dog and man.

The dog, in order to search for his master, must sense the odor of his master—must have formed a psychological attachment. This has been the underlying factor in all the early training: the human handling at birth; the gentle but firm orders; the routine of petting, playing, training, and feeding; the rewards for a good performance—praise, affection, and the anticipated bit of food.

Père Econome said: "It is almost automatic. There is much close exercise of master and dog together. The dogs get meat if they exercise well. They are caressed and praised. This is the first phase—the establishment of a close relationship."

In the *dressage* the first duty of the dog is to find his master on the bare earth without snow.

When the dog has developed facility in finding his master, then he must find two men: his master and a stranger, who is hidden beneath him, as in a landslide.

Later on, this search will be transferred to the snow. But for now—having been taught always to find his master, then a stranger—the dog must also find objects touched by these men: a key, a handkerchief, some piece of clothing.

This is normal training, and the dog that accomplishes it is now ready for the next phase of instruction—finding objects under the snow. Slowly, step by step, the dog learns that he is to find people under the snow.

First, the master covers himself with a little snow. The

*Snow training: a dog being taught to locate
a buried avalanche victim*

dog must learn to scrape the snow away. More and more snow is added, until the man is completely submerged in about three feet of snow. When the dog can always locate his master completely hidden under the snow, he is ready for the big "cave."

A cave is a man-made hole in the snow. Roomy, so that a man can move about, it is supplied with air through a small opening. A man can survive in such a cave, completely buried six to nine feet under the snow, for about thirty minutes. Now the dog must find his way to the cave and find his master inside.

The test is repeated many times, until the dog never makes a mistake in locating the cave.

The dog is ready for the next step of training. Now he must find not only his master inside the cave and under the snow, but he must search for the unknown second man— who is buried beneath his master, also under the snow. The second man might be buried thirteen to twenty feet deep.

Last in the training, the dog must find an unknown person, alone, without the master. This final step accomplished, the dog at last has learned he must find *anyone* under the snow.

He must also learn to find objects in the snow—the only clue to a lost person. Objects which have *not* been touched by his master, but which are buried beneath the snow, and which may lead to someone in need of help.

When a man is buried six feet down, it takes twenty minutes until the human odor can be detected by the dog.

The deeper a man is buried, the longer it takes to find him before the digging-out operation can begin.

Père Econome described the achievements of dogs in each of the three classes of training as follows:

The *Debutante* St. Bernard rescue dog can look for a man within an area of 267 square feet and down to 6½ feet deep in snow.

The *Middle* title is earned when a St. Bernard rescue dog will search for a man over an area of 856 square feet and 6 to 10 feet in depth.

The *Elite* title is earned when he can search for a man in an area of 1,284 square feet and a depth of 6 to 10 feet and can also find objects down 2¾ feet in the snow.

The highly trained dog will work, patiently and steadily, to find the victim of the avalanche. When he does locate the man, he digs a hole with his paws, so that the person can breathe, and the dog tries to uncover him. But right behind the dog is his master-trainer, with a shovel, to speed the rescue. The preferred procedure is for the dog to locate the victim, dig the hole, and allow his master to do the work of getting the victim out. A dog cannot determine the kind of injury suffered by the person under the slide, and overly energetic, though gentle, pulling might cause additional physical damage.

"It is important that the dog has the opportunity to locate the cave by smell," said Père Econome. Normally a dog picks up a scent on the wind and follows it to its source. The master follows directly behind him. The dog traces and retraces the area, systematically going back and forth over the snow, covering each inch of space.

When the dogs work they run absolutely free. There is no harness, saddle, or keg, or anything else that would hamper them in the snow. The masters do allow the dogs to carry things in their mouths, just for the exercise, but when they work, they are free.

The dog and his master apply for their license for avalanche rescue work together.

Père Econome believes that the St. Bernard is superior in avalanche rescue to other types because:

1. The St. Bernard is a calm and steady worker.

2. In a pack he is easy to guide and direct.

3. A single man can make a ski run with a whole pack of St. Bernards, and the man can always be in control of the dogs, without harness, lead rope, or whip.

4. St. Bernards do not bite; they do not attack; they remain together. (In all their history there has been only that one mysterious tragedy.)

5. St. Bernards are sweet and gentle in character, easy to manage, and can learn to do what is necessary *without* orders.

So the training program continues, coordinated now with the rescue work for emergencies due to slides and avalanches, and skiing accidents. Wherever there is an avalanche the St. Bernard dogs will be sent to work with their masters.

Then Père Econome, one of those masters, had a surprise for us. He said: "We are going to stage a rescue for you."

17 *

The Rescue

WHILE WE HAD been sitting in the sunlit rectory and learning about the details of the step by step training of the St. Bernard, from *Debutante* to *Middle* and *Elite*, we had noticed a group of men in jumpsuits, digging.

It had seemed like a strange occupation, there in the middle of the ski run, for some young Italian skiers were slaloming down the mountain side, and around the group of seminarians casually shoveling snow. From the window we could see the activity and what seemed to be a big black hole, which had been steadily growing wider and wider as we talked.

Finally the hole was roomy enough for a man to stay buried in it for a full half-hour. This was a "cave." One young man climbed inside, and his brothers shoveled the snow on top of him. They raked over the snow; then walked all over the ski run. They had the skiers slide near the hole, and after much stomping of many boots, the hill-

Nineteenth-century portrait of a St. Bernard

side looked smooth again, undisturbed, unmarked by any digging.

We had watched it all, unaware that this was being done for us.

We came out of the Hospice as the seminarians were walking to the top of the run and crisscrossing over the snow. Then they returned to the kennel. Fifteen minutes later Père Econome loaned us each a pair of ski boots from the boot chest, and we set out for the ski run. It was hard to keep up with his swift athletic stride, especially in boots too big, but we managed to climb onto a rock from which Gisela could most easily take the pictures of the staged rescue which appear on the following three pages.

Bari was a prima donna of a dog, a celebrity. The trip from the kennel to the cave took much longer than anticipated. Everyone along the way had to shake his paw, or pat his head, and ask a question or two. An admiring entourage formed around him and followed him as he was led down to the edge of the lake.

Bari stood there with a young canon beside him. Then the monk said something to him, and the dog was off.

He picked up a scent. He ran back and forth across the snow-covered mountain. He crisscrossed among the skiers, who had stopped now to watch, too. He ran over the snow so lightly! Here, there, he went with his nose to the ground. He was no longer a relaxed dog. He was alive now, every muscle keyed to the search, tensed.

People poured onto the hillside from all around as news of the rescue performance spread. They stood around with cameras in hand, shooting pictures of Bari searching the snow.

Everyone was awed by this hunt of a dog for a man. The legend was being re-enacted. How lucky to see it happen and not to be a victim—to sit safely on the sidelines, watching!

Silently, the dog sped across the snow, turning only once to see if he was being followed. He sniffed again. He stopped. He gave a single loud, short bark. Now everyone broke into a run as he began to paw the snow. The young monk was right behind him, with his shovel; as Bari pawed, the monk dug. Then, laughing, he had to hold the dog back physically. For this time it was all play. The dog was trying to work his way right into the hole. Quickly the canon shoveled a wider opening, and a laughing face emerged from the cave. The man was rescued.

Bari had found his master. He was wild with joy. The monk gave him the shovel to hold in his mouth.

Père Econome laughed. "He will be a great rescuer."

Then they all marched back to the kennels. The other seminarians carried their shovels over their shoulders. Bari still held in his mouth the one he had earned. The dog had to stop to accept a pat, a kiss from a little girl, and a handshake from an old man. He never dropped the shovel.

The dog was relaxed again. He trotted leisurely. All the tenseness had been worked out. Now there was just fun. The cave had been only a game; he had earned praise, a bit of food, much petting. But when Bari went out in earnest, in the face of real danger, he would work oblivious to the white death all around, searching to save a human life.

"The work of the dogs will go on as long as there is need," said Père Econome, smiling. He knew he had given us a great show.

"Your real name, Père Econome, what is it?" I asked.

"Bernard," he answered, "Bernard Cretton."

18 *

Dogs Look Up to You

THERE IS an old saying:

> Cats look down on you,
> Dogs look up to you,
> But pigs is equal.

Whether pigs are equal or not is still to be tested, though research indicates that they are smarter than one thinks. And since scientists first put a cat in a box, they know anything can be expected to happen.

Certainly dogs have been looking up to men ever since they set off together on their long walk to civilization.

Man and dog have been keeping steady company for thousands of years. Since the beginnings of the relationship, ten thousand years ago, there have been four hundred generations of men and four thousand generations of dogs.

Dogs have developed in a variety of ways—from a pet as small as a hairless Chihuahua, a lap dog of a few pounds, to a dog as large as a man, the great St. Bernard, at least 160 pounds in weight and often more. But no matter how large or how small, whether a tiny pet or a giant shepherd dog, all have one thing in common: they all look up to man and where man leads them they will go.

They have adapted or been adapted to man's needs, as war dogs, guard dogs, hunting dogs, sporting dogs, retrievers, sheep dogs, shepherd dogs, household pets, deer trackers, rabbit pointers, bird dogs, police dogs, work dogs —all developed as specialists for man's special needs.

Dogs have gone with man everywhere, from the first dog who followed the first hunter, to the puppy who was born in an early settlement and stayed there forever. They were even the first to go into space. Because man sent them there.

They may be the first to land on the moon—because man wants to journey there, too.

On a high mountain in Switzerland a holy order of men, with the sole purpose of helping travelers safely across the summit of Europe, trained their dogs as aides and helpers in snow and avalanche. From this pilot program of man and mastiff in the service of the mountain, other rescue programs have come into existence.

For this, the St. Bernard dogs and the Fathers who developed and trained them will always be remembered. They are on a high place—the summit—where together they showed what can be done by looking up.

SELECTED BIBLIOGRAPHY

ASH, E. C. *Dogs, History and Development*. London: Ernest Benn, 1927.

BIBBEY, GEOFFREY. *Testimony of the Spade*. New York: Alfred A. Knopf, 1956.

CHANOINE MARQUIS. *Aumonier de l'Hospice les chiens du Grand St. Bernard et leurs sauvetages*. 1963.

CLARK, J. G. D. *Excavations at Star Carr*. Cambridge, England: The University Press, 1952.

CLUTTON-BROCK, JULIET. "Origins of the Dog." Unpublished manuscript, London, 1962.

CRISLER, L. *Arctic Wild*. New York: Harper and Co., 1958.

DARWIN, CHARLES. *The Variation of Animals and Plants Under Domestication*. New York: Appleton, 1900.

DEGERBØL, MAGNUS. *On a Find of a Preboreal Domestic Dog*. Copenhagen: University of Copenhagen Press, 1961.

DENLINGER, MILO; HEIM, ALBERT; *et al. The New, Complete St. Bernard*. New York: Howell, 1963.

LOGES, CHRÉTIEN DE. *Essai historique sur le Mont St. Bernard*. Geneva, 1789.

LONDON, JACK. *Call of the Wild*. New York: Macmillan, 1903.

————. *White Fang*. New York: Macmillan, 1933.

MOWAT, FARLEY. *Never Cry Wolf*. New York: Dell, 1965.

MURIE, ADOLPH. "The Wolves of Mt. McKinley," No. 5 in the "Fauna of the National Parks of the United States" series. Washington: U.S. Government Printing Office, 1944.

SCOTT, JOHN PAUL and FULLER, JOHN L. *Genetics and the Social Behavior of the Dog*. Chicago: University of Chicago Press, 1965.

ZEUNER, F. E. *History of Domesticated Animals*. London: Hutchinson, 1963.

INDEX

131

Index